D1536556

Electronics Workbench®

The electronics lab in a computer™

Version 4

Macintosh User's Guide

INTERACTIVE IMAGE TECHNOLOGIES LTD.

Disclaimer and Acknowledgements

In no event shall Interactive Image Technologies.Ltd. be liable for any loss of profit or any other commercial damage, including but not limited to special, incidental, consequential or other damages, resulting from or in any way connected with the use of this guide or software. Interactive Image Technologies Ltd. specifically disclaims any other warranties, expressed or implied, including but.not limited to the implied warranties of merchantability and fitness for a particular purpose.

The Interactive Logo and Electronics Workbench are registered trademarks of Interactive Image Technologies Ltd.
Macintosh is a registered trademark of Apple Computer, Inc. All other trademarks are the property of their owners.

No part of this publication may be reproduced, stored in a retrieval system, or transmitted, in any form or by any means, electronic, mechanical, photocopying, recording, scanning, digitizing, or otherwise, without the prior written consent of Interactive Image Technologies Ltd. This publication and the accompanying software are copyrighted and therefore protected by law in Canada, in the United States, and under international treaty provisions.

ISBN 1-55169-008-X

© 1990, 1993, 1995 Interactive Image Technologies Ltd. All rights reserved.
Published September 1995. Printed in Canada.

Preface
About the Documentation Set

Electronics Workbench documentation consists of several volumes, a Quick Start/Installation Card and a Product Support Card.

Electronics Workbench User's Guide

This manual introduces you to the Electronics Workbench interface and, using tutorials, shows you how to use the mouse and menus to build and test analog and digital circuits. It also contains descriptions of each menu and its items.

Electronics Workbench Technical Reference

This manual provides detailed descriptions of all components and instruments for both analog and digital circuits. It also explains some of the factors entering into the simulation of digital and analog circuits, and some of the mathematical models and techniques used.

Quick Start/Installation Card

This gives you the essentials for building and testing circuits, including system requirements, installation instructions and getting help information. Use it if you want to start exploring on your own immediately, or keep it as a handy reference.

Product Support Card

This gives you numerous ways to contact us for free, unlimited support, including phone, fax, email, BBS and Compuserve information. Also included are some common questions with answers and a listing of error messages with solutions.

Other Support Materials

Quick Reference Card identifies component symbols and test instrument icons, plus lists menu commands and keyboard shortcuts.

On-Screen Help (available from the Help menu) provides comprehensive on-the-spot information. You can browse through Help using its table of contents, search for specific topics in its index, or get specific information about a selected component or instrument.

Sample Circuits (found in the Samples folder) include typical analog and digital circuits. They are there for you to examine, modify and use as building blocks in other circuits.

Bulletin Board Services allow you to ask questions, check the latest product information, and upload or download circuits. For details see the Product Support Card.

User Support (if you have a problem or question that can't be solved using the above resources) is available by contacting us. Follow the directions on the Product Support Card.

Release Notes include information on recent changes or additions to the product. These notes can be found online in the Read Me icon created during the installation process.

Table of Contents

Getting Started

Tutorials

Reference

Appendices

Getting Started

Chapter 1
The Electronics Lab in a Computer

This chapter provides an overview of Electronics Workbench. It also suggests ways of using this guide and other support materials to help you start building and testing circuits with Electronics Workbench.

Chapter 1
The Electronics Lab in a Computer

Welcome to Electronics Workbench

Electronics Workbench is an electronics lab in a computer. You can easily build an analog or digital circuit schematic, attach simulated test instruments, and turn on the power to see how it works. Circuit behavior is simulated realistically, and the results are quickly displayed on the multimeter, oscilloscope, Bode plotter, logic analyzer or whatever instruments you have attached to the circuit.

Building and Testing Circuits

As its name implies, Electronics Workbench is modeled on a real electronics workbench. The large central workspace is like the breadboard, the parts bin is beside it, and the parts bin buttons and test instruments are stored on a shelf along the top. You build and test circuits entirely on the workspace using the mouse and menus. Everything you need is readily at hand.

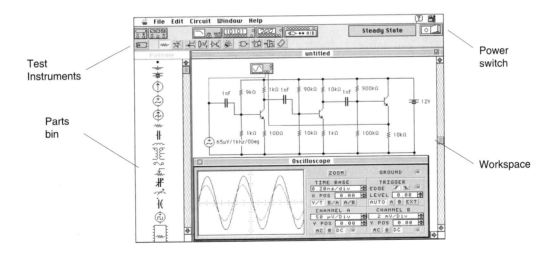

Why Use an Electronics Lab in a Computer?

Defective parts, limited access to instruments and the possibility of accidents are part of life in a real electronics lab. Electronics Workbench not only removes these disadvantages, it provides powerful computational tools that go beyond what is found in a real lab.

It's cost effective. Equipping an electronics workbench or laboratory can be expensive. Electronics Workbench simulates a lab at a fraction of the cost. And the endless supply of unbreakable components reduces the ongoing cost of materials.

It's a time saver. Building and testing circuits using Electronics Workbench is amazingly fast. If you have limited access to a real electronics lab, you can make the most of it by designing and testing circuits first with Electronics Workbench.

It's powerful. Since circuit behavior can be represented by mathematical models, and computers are good at math, using computers to simulate the activity of circuits makes a lot of sense. You can get accurate results quickly for most circuits. Plus, you'll be able to use a Bode plotter (for frequency analysis) and a logic converter (for conversion of truth tables and Boolean functions) which go beyond the capabilities of real test instruments.

It's safe. Learning from mistakes can be instructive, but when the subject matter is electronics, it's also dangerous. With Electronics Workbench you can experiment safely, without fear of getting electrical shocks or damaging equipment.

It's accurate. Real components often do not have the values they are supposed to have. For example, a 10-kΩ resistor is not exactly 10 kΩ, and two "identical" transistors may not be exactly the same. In Electronics Workbench, components are ideal, so the simulated values are the same as your calculated values.

It uses SPICE models. Electronics Workbench is based on industry-standard SPICE models for nonlinear analog components. You can choose from ideal or real-world models, or create your own models. You have complete control over the values and parameters of all components in a circuit.

It's enjoyable and easy to use. You'll soon discover this for yourself!

Does Electronics Workbench Replace a Real Workbench?

If you are mainly interested in electronics theory, or if you don't have access to an electronics laboratory, Electronics Workbench can replace a real electronics workbench. But for hands-on experience, you'll want to use Electronics Workbench in conjunction with a real lab. Here are some ways you can integrate Electronics Workbench with a real workbench.

Pre-construction design and testing: Make the most of your lab time by designing and testing circuits beforehand with Electronics Workbench. Problems can be solved on the computer first, so the circuits you build should work as expected.

Dynamic presentations: Electronic principles and practices can be demonstrated quickly and easily using Electronics Workbench. Trying to illustrate the dynamics of electronics using a static medium such as a chalkboard, flip chart or overhead projector can be difficult and clumsy. Your presentations will come to life as you simulate circuits and instruments with Electronics Workbench. Many devices are available to project the computer screen for an audience.

Creating circuit diagrams: Even if all you want to do is prepare circuit schematics, you can save time by creating them with Electronics Workbench. If you are using System 7, or if you have a screen-capture utility, you can then take a snapshot of the screen and place it in an application that accepts graphics.

Overview

Transient and Steady-State Analysis

When a signal is first applied to a real circuit, there is a short-lived transient state before it settles down to its usual response. Electronics Workbench lets you analyze either the transient or steady-state response of a circuit.

Parts Bin

There are multiple parts bins which include an unlimited supply of components, plus independent and controlled sources. Its components are determined by the parts bin button chosen. Using the parts bin is explained in Chapter 2: User Interface.

The parts bins include a basic parts bin (RLC and sources), active(diodes, transistors, opamps and thyristors), FET, control (switches and controlled sources), hybrid (DAC, ADC, 555 timer and monostable), indicator (bulb, buzzer, LED), digital gates, combinational devices (adder, multiplexer, encoder), sequential devices (flip-flops, counter, shift register) and customized parts bin. You can have a different customized parts bin for each schematic.

Oscilloscope

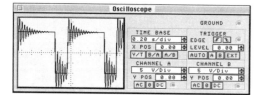

The simulated dual-channel oscilloscope behaves like the actual instrument. It supports internal or external triggering on either the positive or negative edge, and the time base is adjustable from seconds to nanoseconds. You can even study hysteresis by plotting the signal magnitudes on the axes. You can also enlarge the oscilloscope to see details and to get exact readings.

Function Generator

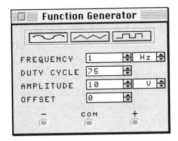

The function generator produces sine, triangular or square waves. You can control the signal's frequency, duty cycle, amplitude and DC offset.

Bode Plotter

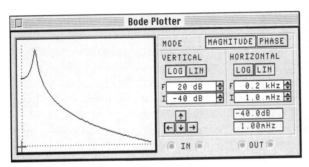

Use the Bode plotter to study the frequency response of a circuit. When you specify the frequencies of interest, the plotter sweeps through them and plots the voltage gain or phase shift against the frequency. The plot can be displayed on either a logarithmic or linear scale.

Multimeter

Of course, no lab would be complete without a multimeter. The simulated multimeter measures DC or AC voltage and current, as well as resistance and decibel loss.

Word Generator

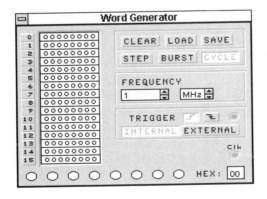

The word generator can drive a digital circuit by producing streams of 16 8-bit words. It can be configured to step one word at a time, burst through the 16 words, or cycle continuously.

Logic Analyzer

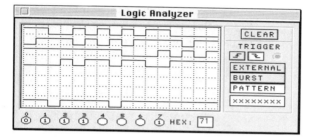

The logic analyzer provides a graphical as well as a hexadecimal display. It can be triggered internally or externally, and on either the negative or positive edge. The logic analyzer can even be configured to wait for a specified pattern before displaying the signals.

Logic Converter

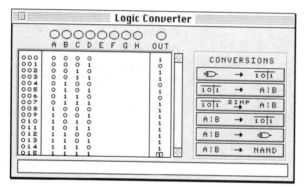

The logic converter is a unique instrument that can convert among gate, truth table and Boolean logic representations. This means you can build a circuit and then read its truth table and Boolean representation. Type in a Boolean expression or truth table and generate a circuit that implements it. Or, build a circuit and have the logic converter simplify it using the Quine-McCluskey method.

How Does Electronics Workbench Compare with Other Simulators?

For anyone trying to build circuits or understand circuit behavior, Electronics Workbench is more powerful and easier to use than any other electronics simulator in its class.

Use familiar schematics rather than abstract netlists. With Electronics Workbench, you create circuit schematics that look just the same as thoseyou're already familiar with on paper—plus you can flip the power switch so the schematic behaves like a real circuit. With other electronics simulators, you may have to type in SPICE node lists as text files—an abstract representation of a circuit beyond the capabilities of all but advanced electronics engineers.

Unique simulated instruments add realism. A realistic multimeter, function generator, oscilloscope and Bode plotter are at your disposal to test analog circuits. For digital circuits you can use a voltmeter, word generator, logic analyzer and logic converter. No other electronics simulator provides simulated test instruments.

Build and test simultaneously. Everything you need is visible, handy and under your control. With other electronics simulators you may have to run three separate programs: one for building, another for simulating, and a third for graphing the results. But in Electronics Workbench you build and test directly on the workbench. You get immediate feedback and can quickly make revisions and test again. In fact, the instrument readings reflect changes as you make them.

Plus all the standard features you expect:

- Choose from a comprehensive selection of either analog and digital components.

- Specify a value or model for each component.

- Create your own subcircuits and analog component models.

- Print circuits together with their instrument readings, parts lists, descriptions and other pertinent information.

- Customize your parts bin and screen layout.

- Watch wires routed neatly and instantly.

Chapter 2
User Interface

In this chapter, you'll find information about using the mouse and menus to build and test circuits and customize the workspace and parts bin. Aspects of the user interface such as using windows, dialog boxes and the Clipboard correspond to Macintosh standards. For information about such functions, consult your *Macintosh User's Guide*.

Chapter 2
User Interface

Working with Components

The different components needed for analog and digital circuits appear in the parts bin along the left side of the workspace. Components are described in the Electronics Workbench User's Reference. Here are basic procedures for working with components.

Placing on the Workspace

The first step in building a circuit is to place components on the workspace.

➤ To use a component, first open the part bin that contains that component by clicking on a parts bin button at the top of the display. Point to one of the components in the parts bin, press and hold the mouse button, and drag it to the workspace. (If you can't see the component you want, drag the scroll box on the right side of the parts bin until it comes into view.)

➤ To delete a component, drag it back to the parts bin (this does not have to be the same parts bin it originally came from). To delete two or more components, select them and choose Delete from the Edit menu.

Tip If you drag two components off the workspace, you'll scroll the workspace instead of deleting the components.

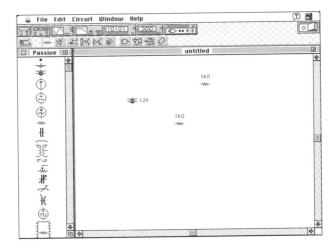

Selecting

As you create circuits, you will often want to select components in order to perform actions on them, such as moving, labeling, or setting values. There are several ways to select.

Clicking to Select

➤ To select a component, point to it so the pointer becomes a hand, and click the mouse button.

➤ Select additional components by shift-clicking. (To shift-click, press and hold the SHIFT key before clicking the mouse button.)

Select the first component by clicking with the mouse button. The component should highlight.

Select additional components by holding down the SHIFT key before clicking.

Tip A selected component highlights so it is easily identified.

Tip Clicking a component's terminal does not select the component. Instead, the terminal highlights, indicating that you can drag a wire from it. You can lock terminals by pressing the OPTION key. Locking terminals makes selecting components (particularly connectors) easier.

Dragging to Select

If you want to select a group of components, you can draw a rectangle around them.

➤ To select a group of components, point above and beside them. Press and hold the mouse button and drag downward diagonally. As you drag, a rectangle appears. Release the mouse button when the rectangle encloses everything you want to select.

Point above and beside the components you want to select.

Press and hold the mouse button, and drag diagonally until the components are enclosed in the rectangle. Then release the mouse button.

➤ To select more components, draw another rectangle while pressing the SHIFT key.

Deselecting

➤ If you have selected a number of components, you can deselect one of the group by pressing the SHIFT key before clicking it.

➤ To deselect everything, click an empty spot on the workspace.

To deselect one of the selected components, hold down the SHIFT key, and then click the component.

To deselect everything, click an empty spot on the workspace.

Moving

You can move components one at a time, or you can select a group and move them all at once. Wires are rerouted automatically.

➤ To move one component, point to it so the pointer becomes a hand, press and hold the mouse button, and drag.

Tip Make sure the pointer looks like a hand before you try to move a component. Otherwise you may drag a wire from a terminal instead. You can lock terminals by pressing the OPTION key.

➤ To move a number of components at once:

1. Select the components using one of the methods described in the previous section.

2. Point to one of the components so the pointer becomes a hand.

3. Press and hold the mouse button, and drag the entire selection.

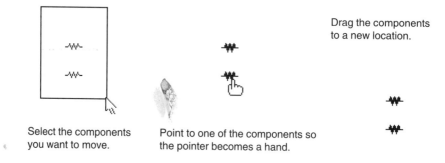

Drag the components to a new location.

Select the components you want to move.

Point to one of the components so the pointer becomes a hand.

➤ To move a component one pixel at a time, select it and press one of the four arrow keys on the keyboard—a useful technique for straightening jagged wires. (Make sure "Delay Until Repeat" in the Keyboard control panel is not turned off.)

Tip If "Grid" is turned on in the Preferences dialog box, component terminals are aligned with points on the grid. You can show or hide the grid, or turn it off altogether, by choosing Preferences from the Circuit menu.

Rotating, Copying and Removing

➤ To change the orientation of a component, select it and choose Rotate from the Circuit menu. The component will turn clockwise 90 degrees.

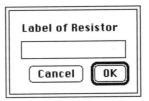

Select the component
and choose Rotate
from the Circuit menu.

The component turns 90°.

➤ To remove or duplicate a component, select it and use the Cut, Copy, Paste and Delete commands in the Edit menu. See Chapter 6: Menu Reference for information on each command.

Tip You can also remove components by dragging them back to the parts bin one at a time.

Setting Labels, Values and Models

Each component can have a label. Some components also have a value (for simple components) or model (for complex components).

➤ To label a component, select it and choose Label from the Circuit menu. (Double-clicking connectors and ground components also displays the Label box.)

```
Label of Resistor

[                    ]

  [ Cancel ]   [ OK ]
```

➤ To set a value or model for an analog component, select it and choose Value or Model from the Circuit menu. Or double-click the component.

➤ To hide or show a circuit's labels, values or models, choose Preferences from the Circuit menu and select the options you want.

For more information on the Label, Value and Model commands, see Chapter 6: Menu Reference.

Wiring

➤ To wire components together:

1. Point to a terminal (a short protruding line) so it highlights, press and hold the mouse button, and drag so a wire appears.

2. Drag the wire to a terminal on a component.

3. When the terminal highlights, release the mouse button. The wire is routed at right angles, without overlapping other components or instrument icons.

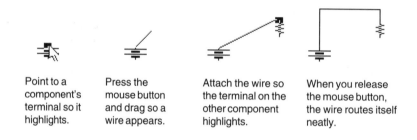

| Point to a component's terminal so it highlights. | Press the mouse button and drag so a wire appears. | Attach the wire so the terminal on the other component highlights. | When you release the mouse button, the wire routes itself neatly. |

Tip You will find it easier to wire components if they are well spaced, not crowded together.

Inserting Components into a Circuit

➤ To insert a component into an existing circuit, align its terminals with the wire and release the mouse button. If there is not enough room for the component, it will remain on top of the wire, without being inserted.

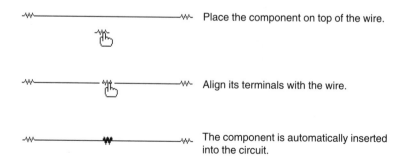

Place the component on top of the wire.

Align its terminals with the wire.

The component is automatically inserted into the circuit.

Removing Components from a Circuit

➤ To remove a component, simply click on it and press the DELETE key.

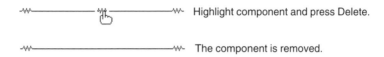

Connecting Two or More Wires

Wires are connected using a connector from the parts bin. If you drag a wire to where you want it to connect to another wire, a connector is automatically created when you release the mouse. You can also insert the connector into an existing circuit, and then drag another wire to one of its free terminals. Or, place the connector on the workspace where you plan to make a connection, and drag wires to itsterminals. You can join up to four wires with one connector.

Connectors will disappear automatically when they are no longer needed. As an example, if the connector is in the middle of a straight wire, it will disappear. However, labelled components do not disappear automatically.

Changing the Color of a Wire

New wires are black, but you can make them different colors. In a complex circuit, colored wires can be distinguished more easily. As well, waveforms on the oscilloscope and logic analyzer are the same color as their probes, so you can correlate input with the resulting instrument display more easily.

➤ To change a wire's color, select it and choose Wire Color from the Circuit menu. Or double-click the wire. Then choose a new color from the dialog box.

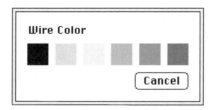

Tip If your computer has a monochrome monitor, or if the Monitor control panel is set to black and white or 4-color, you cannot change the color of the wires.

Straightening a Wire

If a wire is jagged or circuitous, there are several things you can do to make it neater.

➤ If one of the components is out of line, select it and press an arrow key to align it.

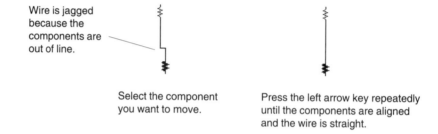

Wire is jagged because the components are out of line.

Select the component you want to move.

Press the left arrow key repeatedly until the components are aligned and the wire is straight.

➤ Sometimes a wire is awkward because it is attached to a terminal pointing in the wrong direction. You can fix this by rotating the component using the Rotate command in the Circuit menu. In the case of a connector, try reconnecting the wire to a terminal that is closer to the other component.

➤ If two wires cross in a way that makes them hard to follow, move one of the components attached to the wire either by dragging it or by selecting it and pressing an arrow key. Or, make one of the wires a different color by selecting it and choosing Wire Color from the Circuit menu.

➤ If a component is between the two components you are wiring together, the wire may be drawn directly through it or rerouted around it. Move the obstructing component out of the way, then adjust the position of one of the two components you are wiring together.

➤ The way a wire is routed sometimes depends on the terminal from which the wire was dragged. Try disconnecting an awkwardly routed wire and then rewire from the opposite terminal.

Tip The workspace grid determines the positions at which components and wires can be placed. For information on the grid, see "Preferences" in Chapter 6: Menu Reference.

Working with Instruments

There are seven test instruments, each represented by an icona small picture of the instrument that you attach to test points in a circuit. The icons are stored on the instrument shelf, above the workspace.

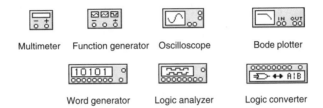

Multimeter   Function generator   Oscilloscope   Bode plotter

Word generator   Logic analyzer   Logic converter

Instruments are described in the Electronics Workbench Technical Reference. Here are basic procedures for working with them.

Using an Instrument Icon

➤ To place an instrument on the workspace, point to its icon on the instrument shelf, and drag it to the workspace.

➤ Select or move an instrument icon the same way you select or move a component (described earlier in this chapter).

➤ To attach an instrument icon to a circuit, point to a terminal so it highlights, and drag a wire out. Attach the wire to a component.

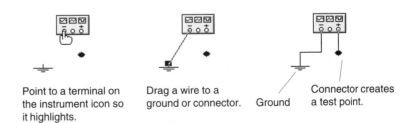

Point to a terminal on the instrument icon so it highlights.

Drag a wire to a ground or connector.   Ground

Connector creates a test point.

Setting Instrument Controls

➤ To see an instrument, select its icon and choose Zoom from the Circuit menu. Or double-click the instrument icon.

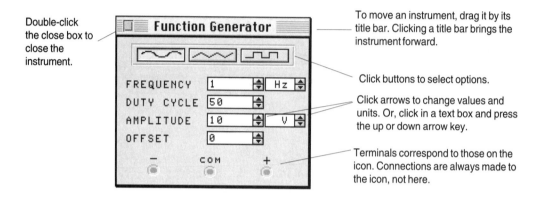

Double-click the close box to close the instrument.

To move an instrument, drag it by its title bar. Clicking a title bar brings the instrument forward.

Click buttons to select options.

Click arrows to change values and units. Or, click in a text box and press the up or down arrow key.

Terminals correspond to those on the icon. Connections are always made to the icon, not here.

➤ To select options, click buttons on the instrument.

➤ To change values or units, click the up or down arrows beside them. On the function generator, oscilloscope and Bode plotter, you can also click in the text box and press the up or down arrow key on the keyboard. For the function generator, word generator and logic analyzer, you can select a value and type a new one.

➤ If an instrument is hidden by another window, bring it forward by clicking its title bar. Double-clicking the instrument icon also brings the instrument to the front. To bring all instruments to the front, choose Bring Instruments To Front from the Window menu.

➤ To move an instrument, drag it by its title bar.

➤ To close an instrument, double-click its Control-menu box.

➤ To remove an instrument, drag its icon back to the instrument shelf. It will close automatically, and any wires attached to it will disconnect.

Turning on the Power

➤ To turn on the power, click the power switch in the top right corner of the display. Clicking the switch again turns off the power.

➤ Clicking the power switch has the same effect as using the Activate command. For more information, see "Circuit➤Activate" in Chapter 6: Menu Reference.

Customizing the Workspace and Parts Bin

Adjusting the Workspace

➤ The workspace is about four times larger than what you see on the display at any one time. There are two ways to scroll it:

- Drag a scroll box or press a scroll arrow in the direction you want to go.

- Select two or more components or instrument icons on the workspace, and then drag them over the workspace edge. The workspace scrolls as you drag.

➤ To move the workspace or parts bin, point to its title bar and drag.

➤ To resize the workspace or parts bin, point to the size box in the bottom right corner, and drag to make the window bigger or smaller. (You can change only the parts bin's length, not its width.)

➤ To neatly arrange the workspace, parts bin and (if it is open) description windows, place them approximately where you want them, and choose Arrange from the Window menu.

Move a
window by
dragging its
title bar.

Drag the scroll
boxes to see more
of the workspace or
parts bin.

Point to a border
and drag to
change the
window's size.

➤ To return the workspace or parts bin to its original place and size, click the maximize box in its upper right corner.

➤ If the workspace or parts bin is covered by another window, click its title bar to bring it forward. Or choose Circuit or Parts Bin from the Window menu.

Customizing the Parts Bins

You can customize a circuit's parts bins in a number of ways:

• Set an analog component's value or model in the parts bin. Then each time you add the component to a circuit, it will have the preset value. Changing a component's value or model in the parts bin doesn't affect the value or model of components already placed on the workspace.

• If you use the subcircuit command in the Circuit menu to create a subcircuit, its icon is added to the bottom of the Custom parts bin automatically.

• You can duplicate a subcircuit and add it to another circuit. Use the Copy command in the Edit menu to copy the subcircuit icon, then use Paste to add it to the workspace or Custom parts bin of the other circuit.

Customizing the Workspace and Parts Bin for All Circuits

You can add parts and/or subcircuits to the Custom parts bin. There are three reasons why you'd want to do this:

- Sometimes you will make a subcircuit that you would like in the parts bin each time you start Electronics Workbench for easy reuse.

- You might want a different default value for one of the components. For example, you may want the batteries to always default to 10 V instead of 12 V. If you copy the battery to the Custom bin, you can change its default value permanently.

- You might want to put your most frequently used parts in the Custom bin so you do not need to keep switching bins.

Make the changes to the default circuit. The default circuit is called Default.

Tip If you are working on a network and have your own configuration folder, save your modified default files there. Then your changes affect only your circuits. If you want to change the default files for all users, you may first have to remove a restriction on write privileges. If necessary, get help from your system administrator. For information on setting up configuration directories, see "Network Setup" in Appendix A: System Reference.

Caution

Be sure you have a backup copy of the default circuits before you change them.

Tutorials

Chapter 3
Building and Testing an Analog Circuit

You can learn the basics of using Electronics Workbench in a short time by building and testing a simple circuit. Instructions for using the mouse and menus are given as you go. If you want more information, see Chapter 2: User Interface.

Chapter 3
Building and Testing an Analog Circuit

Orientation

Building and testing circuits in Electronics Workbench is similar to working in a real electronics lab. The big difference is that you use a mouse to choose, wire together and test components. Plus you will never have defective equipment, and everything you need is right at hand.

➤ To start Electronics Workbench, double-click the Electronics Workbench icon in the Electronics Workbench folder.

The *parts bin* along the left side holds an unlimited supply of each component. To fill the bin with a specific type of component, click one of the parts bin buttons which are found at the top of the display, along with the *instruments* and power switch you will need for testing. The large central area is the *workspace*, on which you build and test circuits. You can use an unlimited number of components in a circuit, and you can combine parts of a circuit into reusable subcircuits.

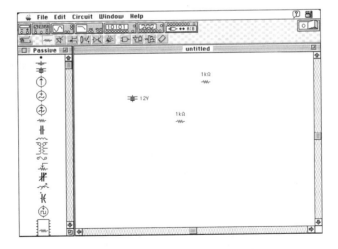

➤ To see all the components in the parts bin, scroll the bin. Point to the scroll box on its right side, press and hold the mouse button, and drag the scroll box downward. Drag it upward to see the components at the top of the bin again.

Getting Context-Sensitive Help

If you are familiar with electronic schematic drawings, you probably recognize the component symbols. If you want more information about a component or test instrument, you can use the on-screen Help system.

➤ To get information about a component or instrument:

1. Select the component or instrument icon you want to know about by pointing to it and pressing the mouse button.

2. Choose Help from the Help menu. (To choose from a menu, point to the menu title, press and hold the mouse button, and drag through the menu to the command you want. Releasing the mouse button chooses the command.)

   You'll see a window with information about the selected component or instrument.

Click the close box to close the window.

Click highlighted text to get related information.

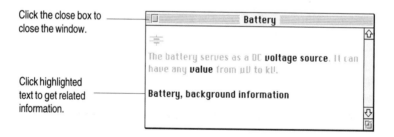

3. If you want information about a related topic, click highlighted text.

4. To close the Help window, click its close box.

Tip If there is more than one Help window open, you can close them all by choosing Close Help Windows from the Help menu.

Getting General Help

When you select a component or instrument icon and choose the Help command, you get specific or "context-sensitive" information about it. If you choose Help when nothing is selected, you will get the Help Table of Contents.

➤ To go to the Help Table of Contents, deselect any selected information by clicking an empty spot on the workspace, then choose Help from the Help menu.

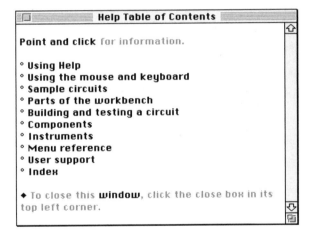

➤ To get a listing of Help topics, choose Help Index from the Help menu.

Tip You can leave Help windows open while you build and test a circuit. If a Help window covers your circuit, drag it out of the way. (To drag a window, point to its title bar, press and hold the mouse button, and move the mouse.) You can also make a window shorter or narrower by dragging the size box in its lower right corner.

For more information, choose How To Use Help from the Help menu for the Help window.

Keyboard Shortcuts

A key or key combination that you press to issue a command is called a "keyboard shortcut." Whenever there is a keyboard shortcut for a command, it appears beside the command in the menu. For example, beside Save in the File menu you'll see ⌘-S. This means that another way to save a circuit is to press and hold the ⌘(Command) key, and then press S key. (If you try this, you'll see a dialog box. For now just click Cancel.)

Building a Circuit

In this tutorial, you will build a simple DC voltage-divider circuit.

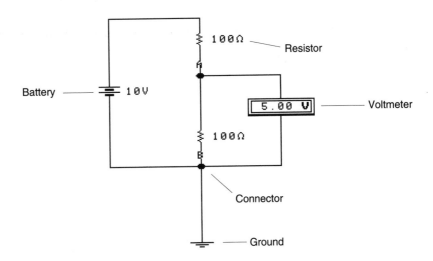

Placing Components on the Workspace

Start by placing a battery, two resistors and a ground on the workspace.

➤ To place a component on the workspace, point to it in the parts bin, press and hold the mouse button, and drag the component where you want it.

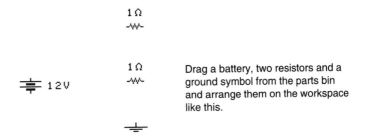

Drag a battery, two resistors and a ground symbol from the parts bin and arrange them on the workspace like this.

➤ If you want to move a component, point to it , press and hold the mouse button, and drag it to a new location.

Help If you want to remove a component, drag it back to the parts bin. Or, select it and choose Delete from the Edit menu.

Rotating Components

Now rotate the resistors so they can be wired neatly into the circuit. Each time you rotate a component it turns clockwise 90 degrees.

➤ To rotate a resistor, select it and choose Rotate from the Circuit menu.

Tip You can rotate the two resistors at once by selecting them both, as described below, before choosing Rotate.

Help If the Rotate command is dimmed, the resistor isn't selected. Try again by pointing to it so the pointer becomes a hand, and then click the mouse button.

Selecting More than One Component

Method A. Shift-Clicking

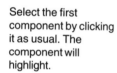

Select the first component by clicking it as usual. The component will highlight.

Select additional components by holding down the SHIFT key before clicking.

Method B. Dragging a Rectangle

Point above and beside the components you want to select.

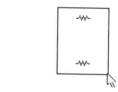

Press and hold the mouse button, and drag diagonally until the rest of the components are in the rectangle that appears.

Deselecting

To deselect one of the selected components, hold down the SHIFT key, then click the component.

To deselect everything, click an empty spot on the workspace.

Wiring Components

Most components have short protruding lines called terminals that highlight when you point to them. You connect components by dragging wires from their terminals.

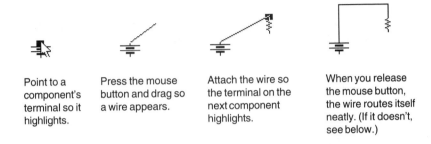

Point to a component's terminal so it highlights.	Press the mouse button and drag so a wire appears.	Attach the wire so the terminal on the next component highlights.	When you release the mouse button, the wire routes itself neatly. (If it doesn't, see below.)

➤ Start by wiring the components as shown below.

Help If you want to disconnect a wire, point to a terminal so it highlights, then drag the wire away. Release the mouse button to remove the wire altogether, or connect it to another terminal.

Straightening a Wire

If a wire is jagged or circuitous, you can try to straighten it by moving or rotating a component to which it is attached.

➤ To make fine adjustments to the position of a component, select it and press an arrow key.

For more details, see "Wiring" in Chapter 2: User Interface.

Connecting Two Wires

To complete this circuit, connect a wire from the battery's negative (lower) terminal to the wire going to the ground component. To join two wires, you use a connector.

About the Connector The round dot in the parts bin is called a *connector.* Use it to connect wires to each other and to create test points in the circuit. A connector can join up to four wires, one on each side.

Connector   A connector can join up to four wires.

➤   Drag a wire from the battery to where you want it to connect to the other wire, and a connector is automatically created when you release the mouse. Or, you can drag a connector from the parts bin and insert it into the wire. Then drag a wire from the battery to the terminal on the connector's left side.

Labeling a Component

Each component in a circuit can be labeled. Try labeling the connector you just created.

➤   To label a component, select it and choose Label from the Circuit menu. You'll see a Label box. In this case, label the connector B, then choose OK.

Help If you can't see the label, the "Show labels" option is probably turned off. To turn it on, choose Preferences from the Circuit menu and click the "Show labels" box so you see an X. Then click Accept.

Tip As a shortcut, you can label connectors and other components that don't have values or models by double-clicking them. (To double-click, point to a component and quickly press the mouse button twice.)

Setting a Component's Value

Each of the components in the parts bin represents a class or type of electrical part, which you can customize to suit your needs. The battery, for example, is preset to 12 V, but this circuit calls for a 10-V battery.

➤ To set the battery's voltage, select it in the circuit and choose Value from the Circuit menu. You'll see a dialog box. Type **10,** then choose Accept.

Tip A quick way to set a component's value is to double-click it.

The units are already set to V, which is what you want for this circuit. If called for, however, you could change the units to kV, mV or μV by clicking the current units and choosing new units from the pop-up menu that appears.

➤ The resistors are preset to 1 kΩ. Change their value to 100 Ω. To save time, select them both before choosing Value from the Circuit menu.

Help If the values do not appear on the workspace, choose Preferences from the Circuit menu and turn on "Show values."

Tip If you want to use a component with the same value many times in a circuit, you can set its value in the parts bin.

Saving a Circuit

➤ To save your circuit:

1. Choose Save from the File menu. You'll see a directory dialog box.

2. Scroll the directory list to see the Tutorial folder, then open it by double-clicking.

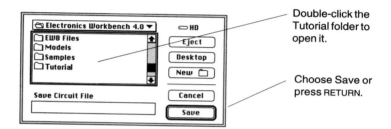

Double-click the Tutorial folder to open it.

Choose Save or press RETURN.

3. Type a name for your circuit. For example, type:

    DC Divider Circuit

4. Choose Save.

Tip If a button has a double border, you can also choose it by pressing RETURN.

Testing a Circuit

Attaching a Voltmeter

This voltage divider circuit calls for a voltmeter to measure voltage across a resistor. You will find the voltmeter near the top of the parts bin. (Unlike the other test instruments, which are stored above the workspace, the voltmeter and ammeter are stored in the parts bin since an unlimited supply is available.)

➤ Attach the voltmeter as shown below. You'll need another connector, which you can label A.

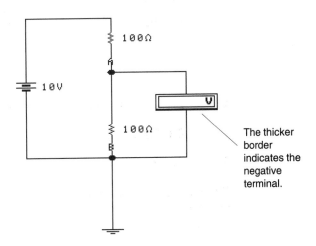

The thicker border indicates the negative terminal.

Tip If a wire runs through a label, you can move the label to the right by adding several spaces before it in the Label dialog box.

The voltmeter is preset to measure DC voltage, and its resistance is preset to 1 MΩ. Both settings are what you want for this circuit. (If you wanted to change the voltmeter's settings, you could select it and choose Value from the Circuit menu, or double-click the voltmeter.)

Activating a Circuit

So far, you've assembled the components, set their values, and wired and grounded the circuit. Now you are ready to activate the circuit by "turning on the power."

➤ To activate a circuit, click the power switch at the top right of the display.

If everything is correct, the voltmeter should read 5.00 V, since two resistors of the same resistance divide the voltage from the battery in half. This illustrates Kirchhoff's voltage law, which states that the arithmetic sum of the voltages around a series circuit equals the applied voltage.

Help If the voltmeter does not read 5.00 V, check the values of the battery and resistors and make sure the circuit is wired properly. Also, double-click the voltmeter and make sure it is set to DC.

Explore If you want to experiment, try changing the resistors' or battery's values and activate the circuit again. You could also add another connector between the battery and upper resistor to create a new test point. Then move the voltmeter's probes and activate the circuit again.

Tip Once you have added connectors to create test points, you can move the voltmeter's probes to different parts of a circuit without having to activate it again. However, if you change the components or their values, re-activate the circuit to get a valid reading.

➤ Save your circuit by choosing Save from the File menu. (It's a good idea to save your work frequently.)

Stopping a Simulation

Simulation usually stops when the circuit has reached steady state. (The status indicator beside the power switch informs you when steady state is reached.)

For this simple circuit, Electronics Workbench can quickly simulate the circuit's behavior and calculate the voltage at each test point. If simulating a circuit requires a longer time and you've seen enough, you can stop the simulation by clicking off the power switch or by pressing ⌘-T.

Trying Out Some More Features

Starting a New Circuit

Practice some of the things you've learned by building another circuit.

➤ To begin building a new circuit, choose New from the File menu. A new workspace will open.

If you have any unsaved changes in your current circuit, you will be asked if you want to save them.

Building a Simple LED Circuit

➤ Try building the simple LED (light-emitting diode) circuit shown below. You'll need two components you haven't used before—an LED and an ammeter. (Remember, if you want information about a component, select it and choose Help from the Help menu.)

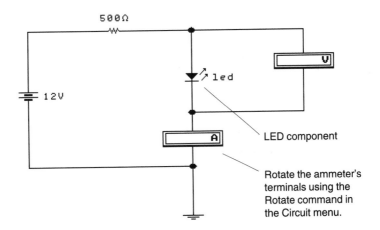

➤ To wire the ammeter neatly in series, rotate its terminals using the Rotate command in the Circuit menu.

➤ Set the resistor to 500 Ω. The battery, LED, voltmeter and ammeter have default settings you can use for now.

➤ Now activate the circuit. The arrows on the LED highlight when the power is turned on. You should get a voltmeter reading of 1.75 V across the LED, and the ammeter should read 20.5 mA.

Changing a Component's Model

Unlike the battery and resistor, whose values you set directly by typing them in, an LED has a number of parameters that together form a model. Electronics Workbench supplies a number of prepackaged models for LEDs and other nonlinear (or complex) components such as diodes and transistors.

➤ Change the LED's model by selecting it and choosing Model from the Circuit menu, or double-click the LED. You'll see a Model dialog box.

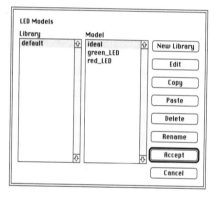

➤ Select the model "red_LED," then choose Accept.

➤ Activate the circuit again. The voltage drop should now be 1.50 V, and the ammeter should read 21.0 mA.

➤ If you want to save this circuit, choose Save from the File menu.

If You Want to Learn More

In the next tutorial, you'll learn how to use the test instruments to analyze a circuit's response. If you want to continue now, turn to Chapter 4.

If you want to do some experimenting on your own at this point, you can start a new circuit by choosing New from the File menu. (See the Summary on the next page for guidance.)

Quitting

➤ When you are ready to leave Electronics Workbench, choose Quit from the File menu.

Summary

➤ To start Electronics Workbench, double-click the Electronics Workbench icon in the Electronics Workbench folder.

➤ To use a component, click on a parts bin button to fill the parts bin. Then drag a component from the bin onto the workspace.

➤ To delete a component, drag it back to the parts bin. Or select it and choose Delete from the Edit menu.

➤ To select a component, point to it and click the mouse button. To select additional components, press SHIFT before clicking them.

➤ To get context-sensitive information, select a component and choose Help from the Help menu. To get general information, make sure nothing is selected before choosing Help.

➤ To connect components, drag a wire from one component's terminal and attach it to the terminal of another component.

➤ To change the orientation of a component, select it and choose Rotate from the Circuit menu.

➤ To label a component, select it and choose Label from the Circuit menu.

➤ To specify a component's value or model, select it and choose Value or Model from the Circuit menu. Or double-click the component.

➤ To hide or show component labels, values or models, choose Preferences from the Circuit menu and adjust the settings.

➤ To activate a circuit, click the power switch.

➤ If you want to stop a simulation, click the power switch again.

➤ To save a circuit, choose Save from the File menu.

Chapter 4
Trying Out the Analog Instruments

In this chapter, you will learn how to open a circuit and test it using the oscilloscope, function generator and Bode plotter. If you haven't done the tutorial in Chapter 3, you might want to do it first. If you are eager to get going, the procedures used to build a circuit are summarized on the previous page.

Chapter 4
Trying Out the Analog Instruments

Opening a Circuit

In this tutorial, you will open an RC (resistive and capacitive) charging circuit provided with Electronics Workbench and test it with the oscilloscope. Then you will replace the battery with the function generator to create a low-pass filter and test the circuit again, this time using the Bode plotter.

➤ If Electronics Workbench is not running, start it.

➤ To open a circuit:

1. Choose Open from the File menu. You will see a directory dialog box.

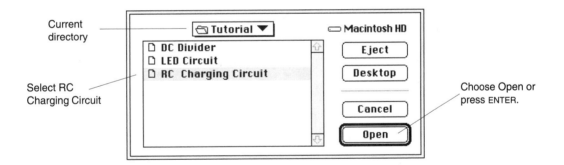

Current directory

Select RC Charging Circuit

Choose Open or press ENTER.

2. If the Tutorial folder is not already open, open it by selecting it and choosing Open. (Or double-click the Tutorial folder.)

3. Select RC Charging Circuit and choose Open. Double-clicking the circuit name also opens it.

You'll see the RC circuit shown below, composed of a 10-V battery, a 10-kΩ resistor, a 20-µF capacitor and a ground component.

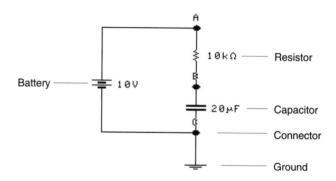

Making a Copy of a Circuit

Make a copy of the circuit so you can work on it without changing the original.

➤ To make a copy of a circuit:

1. Choose Save As from the File menu. A directory dialog box will appear.

2. If you want, open a different folder.

3. Type a name for the new circuit. For example, type:

    My RC Charging Circuit

4. Choose Save.

The original circuit closes, and the newly named circuit remains open.

Trying Out the Oscilloscope

The oscilloscope is one of four test instruments you can use to analyze an analog circuit (not counting the voltmeter and ammeter, which are in the parts bin). The instrument icons are stored on an "instrument shelf" above the workspace. While each has a different function, the way you use the instruments is similar.

Electronics Workbench's oscilloscope looks and acts much like a real dual-channel oscilloscope. It displays the waveforms of one or two electronic signals so you can analyze their magnitude and frequency over a period of time.

Oscilloscope icon

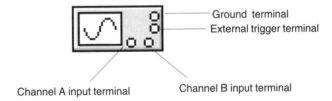

Ground terminal
External trigger terminal

Channel A input terminal   Channel B input terminal

Connecting the Instrument Icon

➤ To place the oscilloscope on the workspace, point to its icon, press and hold the mouse button, and drag it to a place near the circuit.

➤ Connect the oscilloscope icon to the circuit as shown below. To connect an instrument, point to a terminal on its icon so it highlights, then drag out a wire. Attach the wire to a connector in the circuit.

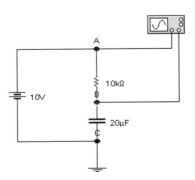

Adjusting the Instrument Controls

To adjust a test instrument's controls, it must be "zoomed open."

➤ To open an instrument, select its icon and choose Zoom from the Circuit menu. Or double-click the instrument icon.

You can drag the instrument anywhere on the display. To close the instrument, double-click its Control-menu box in its top left corner.

➤ For the first analysis, set the oscilloscope's controls as shown below. To adjust an instrument's settings, click the little arrows beside the controls. Or, click in a text box and press the up or down arrow key on your keyboard.

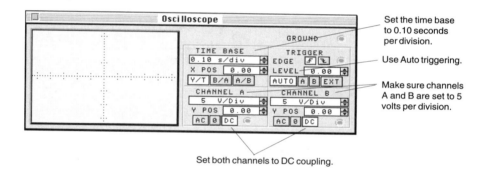

Set the time base to 0.10 seconds per division.

Use Auto triggering.

Make sure channels A and B are set to 5 volts per division.

Set both channels to DC coupling.

Setting the Analysis Options

When a signal is first applied to a real circuit, there is a short-lived transient response before it settles down to its usual steady-state response. With Electronics Workbench, you can analyze either the transient or steady-state response of a circuit. For this RC charging circuit, use transient analysis so you can see its charging curve on the oscilloscope.

➤ To set the analysis options:

1. Choose Analysis Options from the Circuit menu. You will see the Analysis Options dialog box.

2. Select "Transient."

3. Select "Pause after each screen" so an X appears beside it.

Change the Analysis
Type to "Transient."

Change the Oscilloscope
Display to "Pause after
each screen."

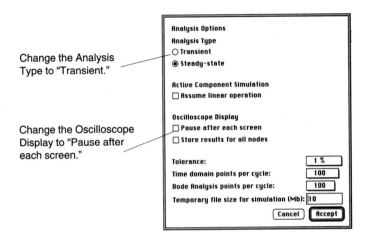

4. Choose Accept.

Observing the Output

➤ To see the circuit output on the oscilloscope, activate the circuit by clicking the power switch in the top right corner. After a few seconds, you should see a charging curve like this.

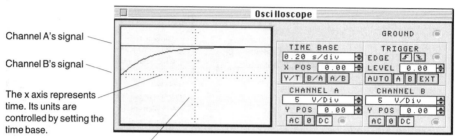

Channel A's signal

Channel B's signal

The x axis represents time. Its units are controlled by setting the time base.

The y axis represents voltage. Its units are controlled by the volts/division setting for channels A and B.

Help If you don't see the charging curve shown above, check the settings on the oscilloscope and make sure you've connected it properly. Also choose Analysis Options from the Circuit menu and make sure "Transient" is selected.

Concept As you may recall, the charging curve demonstrates the RC time constant formula, where one RC time constant (TC or τ) = R (in ohms) x C (in farads). In this case TC = 10 kΩ x 20 μF = 0.2 seconds. Approximately five time constants are needed to fully charge the capacitor, so the charging curve reaches steady state after 0.2 x 5 = 1.0 second. Since the time base is set to 0.10 seconds per division, the charging curve continues over 10 time-base divisions on the scope (1.0/0.10 = 10 time-base divisions).

➤ The simulation pauses when the waveforms fill the oscilloscope screen. To continue the simulation, choose Resume from the Circuit menu, or press ⌘-J.

Most simulations stop automatically once the circuit reaches steady state. To stop a simulation before then, choose Stop from the Circuit menu, press ⌘-T, or click the power switch again.

Explore Try changing the time base to 0.20 s/div. The oscilloscope automatically redraws the waveforms. The charging curve should now take 1.0/0.20 = 5 time-base divisions before it reaches steady state. *Change the time base back to 0.10 before continuing.*

Changing the Color of Wires

To help you identify the waveforms on the oscilloscope, you can make the wires going to channels A and B different colors. When the circuit is activated again, each channel's waveform will be the same color as its wire, so you can easily correlate them. (Using different colors can also help you distinguish wires in a complex circuit.)

➤ To change the color of a wire, select it and choose Wire Color from the Circuit menu. Then choose the color you want from the dialog box that appears. Forexample, make the wire going to channel A red and the wire going to channel B blue.

Tip You can also double-click a wire to change its color.

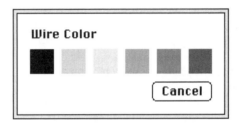

Help If your Macintosh cannot display colors, or if you have changed the Monitors control panel setting to Black & White or 4-color, the Wire Color command is dimmed.

➤ Choose Save from the File menu. (It's a good idea to save your work regularly.)

Changing the Analysis Options

Now try changing the type of analysis used by Electronics Workbench, and compare its effect on the oscilloscope display.

➤ To change the analysis options:

1. Choose Analysis Options from the Circuit menu.

2. Change the analysis to "Steady-state."

3. Turn off "Pause after each screen." (Select it again so an X no longer appears beside it.)

4. Choose Accept.

5. Click the power switch to activate the circuit again. After a few seconds, the oscilloscope displays one flat signal showing the final steady state, without the initial transient charging curve. You see only one signal because the waveforms for channels A and B are superimposed.

6. To separate the signals, change the Y POS value for channel A to 0.40. The signal through channel A will now be plotted higher on the y axis, so it can be seen clearly. (You can make the change while the circuit is being simulated.) Then change Y POS back to 0.00.

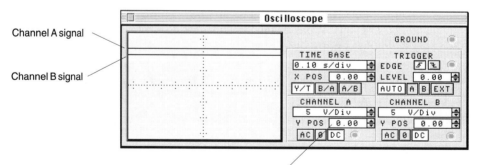

Channel A signal

Channel B signal

Separate the signals by changing the position at
which channel A's signal is plotted on the y axis.

Help If you don't see waveforms on the oscilloscope, try changing the trigger to Auto. (Flat waveforms do not trigger the oscilloscope, so triggering must be automatic.)

Trying Out the Function Generator

Now substitute the function generator for the battery so the circuit has an AC voltage source. With an AC voltage source, the circuit becomes a low-pass filter that allows low-frequency AC waves to pass and blocks or "attenuates" high-frequency waves.

➤ Delete the battery by dragging it back to the parts bin. Or, select it and choose Delete from the Edit menu.

➤ Drag the function generator to the workspace, and connect it as shown at the bottom of the page.

Function generator icon

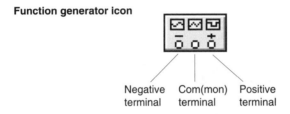

Negative   Com(mon)   Positive
terminal   terminal   terminal

➤ Change the value of the capacitor from 20 µF to 1 µF. (To change a component's value, double-click the component and type a new value. Then click Accept.)

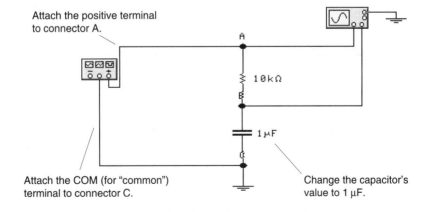

Attach the positive terminal to connector A.

10 kΩ

1 µF

Attach the COM (for "common") terminal to connector C.

Change the capacitor's value to 1 µF.

➤ Double-click the function generator to zoom it open. If it covers the oscilloscope, drag it to a new position.

➤ Change the amplitude setting to 10 V by clicking the up arrow beside Amplitude. (You could also type in a new value or click in the text box and press the up arrow key.)

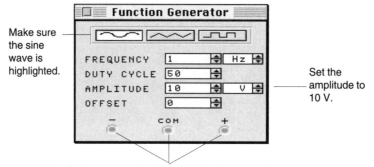

Make sure the sine wave is highlighted.

Set the amplitude to 10 V.

Terminals correspond to those on the instrument icon.
Wires are always attached to the icon, not here.

➤ Change the oscilloscope to AC coupling by clicking AC for both channels.

➤ Activate the circuit. You should see waveforms like these:

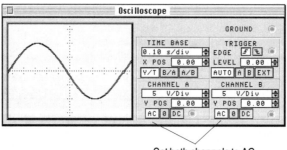

Set both channels to AC.

As you can see, the output waveform at channel B is almost the same as the input waveform at channel A. (At the low frequency of 1 Hz, the low-pass filter has little effect.)

Help If your oscilloscope reading doesn't look like this, check the values of the components and the settings for the function generator and oscilloscope. Also, make sure you have selected "Steady-state" in the Analysis Options dialog box.

Explore If you want to separate the waveforms to see them more clearly, change the Y POS for one of the channels. This shifts the waveform up or down on the y axis. If you want to shift the starting point of the waveforms along the x axis, change the X POS value.

➤ Now increase the frequency of the function generator's AC signal to 1 kHz, and lower the oscilloscope's time base to 0.20 ms/div. (In order to distinguish the waveforms at higher frequencies, it is necessary to lower, or magnify, the time base.)

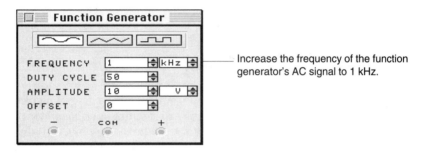

Increase the frequency of the function generator's AC signal to 1 kHz.

➤ Activate the circuit again. Now the waveforms should look like this:

Decrease the time base to 0.20 ms/div.

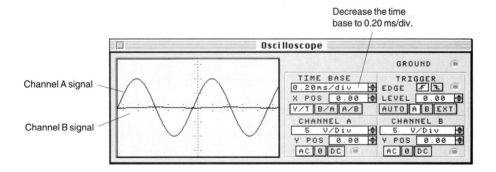

At the increased frequency, the waveform for channel B is greatly attenuated by passing high-frequency waves to ground. This filtering of high-frequency waves is caused by the low reactance of the capacitor at high frequencies, as expressed by the equation:

$$X_c = \frac{1}{2\pi fC}$$

where X_c is reactance
   f is frequency
   C is capacitance

Trying Out the Bode Plotter

The Bode plotter graphs the frequency response of a circuit. It is useful in analyzing the cutoff frequency in circuits such as a low-pass filter. (You won't find a Bode plotter in a real electronics lab, only in a computer simulation. Similar results can be achieved in a lab by attaching a spectrum analyzer to an oscilloscope.)

Bode plotter icon

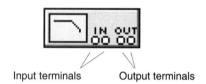

Input terminals   Output terminals

➤ Remove the oscilloscope and replace it with the Bode plotter.

1. To remove the oscilloscope, drag its icon back to the instrument shelf. Its probes disconnect automatically.

2. Drag the Bode plotter to the workspace and connect it as shown below.

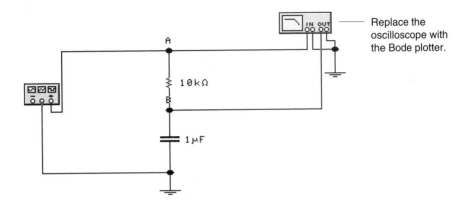

Replace the oscilloscope with the Bode plotter.

➤ Double-click the Bode plotter icon to zoom it open. If it covers something you want to see, drag it out of the way.

➤ Adjust the controls as shown below. Be sure to double-check the units.

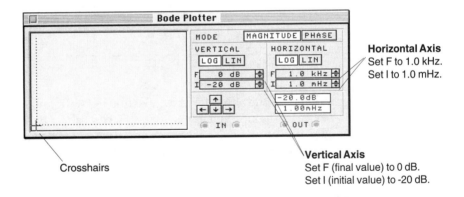

Horizontal Axis
Set F to 1.0 kHz.
Set I to 1.0 mHz.

Vertical Axis
Set F (final value) to 0 dB.
Set I (initial value) to -20 dB.

Crosshairs

➤ Activate the circuit. The Bode plotter begins to generate a series of frequencies starting at the initial value (1.0 mHz) and ending at the final value (1.0 kHz). The status indicator beside the power switch displays the changing frequencies. The Bode plotter then plots the ratio of output voltage to input voltage as a function of frequency.

➤ Drag the crosshair (stored at the left edge of the Bode plotter display) to the half-power point, approximately -3.00 dB, on the plot. Readouts for the crosshair appear in the Bode plotter's lower right corner. The cutoff frequency should be approximately 15.8 Hz.

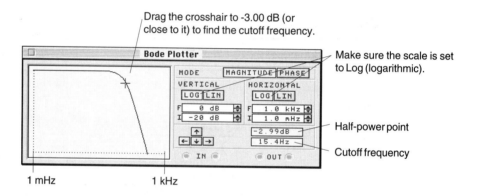

Drag the crosshair to -3.00 dB (or close to it) to find the cutoff frequency.

Make sure the scale is set to Log (logarithmic).

Half-power point

Cutoff frequency

1 mHz   1 kHz

Explore Change the value for the capacitor to 10 μF and check the frequency cutoff again. You can also use the crosshair to find the frequency and magnitude at any point on the graph. Instead of dragging the crosshairs, try moving them using the arrows on the Bode plotter.

Explore If you want to see the ratio of output to input voltage against frequency on a linear scale, choose LIN for both axes. To make the plot easier to interpret, set the vertical scale's initial value to 1 and its final value to 0. (The resulting graph is not technically a Bode plot.)

Describing a Circuit

You can add a description of the circuit for future reference. You might want to include instructions for circuit modifications, test and verification notes, or design ideas.

➤ Close the Bode plotter by double-clicking its close box.

➤ Choose Description from the Window menu, then type in the window that appears. For example, type:

A low-pass filter is an AC circuit that blocks high-frequency waves and passes low-frequency waves.

Explore You can change the description window's size and move it to a different position. If you then choose Arrange from the Window menu, the description and workspace windows will be resized and repositioned neatly, without overlapping each other.

➤ Save your circuit again.

Reposition the windows by dragging their title bars. Then choose Arrange from the Window menu to neatly arrange them.

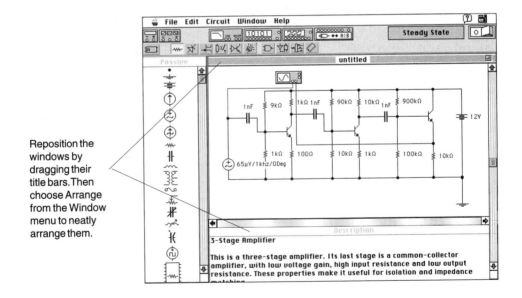

Printing a Circuit

If you have a printer attached to your computer system, you can print a circuit's schematic and other specified data.

➤   To print:

1. Choose Print from the File menu. You will see the Print dialog box.

2. The circuit is automatically selected for printing. Also select Description and Bode Plotter so you see an X beside them.

The circuit's schematic is automatically selected for printing.

Select Description and Bode Plotter.

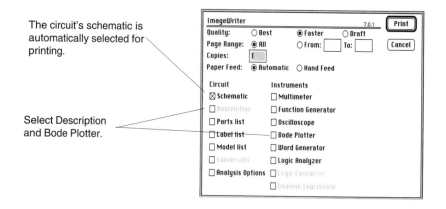

3. Choose Print.

The options in the Print dialog box depend on the kind of printer, printer software, and system software you are using. For more information, see "Print Setup" in Chapter 6: Menu Reference.

The Next Step

If you want to practice what you've learned, try experimenting with the sample circuits included with Electronics Workbench.

➤ To open a sample circuit:

1. Choose Open from the File menu. You'll see a directory dialog box.

2. Open the "Samples" folder and choose a circuit. (Some circuits are organized into two additional folders, labeled "Simple Circuits" and "Faulty Circuits". (Faulty circuits provide opportunities for troubleshooting practice.)

3. If you make changes to a sample circuit, use the Save As command in the File menu to save the circuit with a different name.

If you need guidance as you experiment, you'll find detailed information in the Electronics Workbench Technical Reference. (Save changes to a sample circuit using the Save As command in the File menu.)

Summary

➤ To open a circuit, choose Open from the File menu and use the directory dialog box that appears to choose the circuit you want.

➤ To use a test instrument, drag its icon from the instrument shelf to the workspace.

➤ Attach an instrument icon by dragging wires from its terminals.

➤ Double-click an instrument icon to zoom it open.

➤ To adjust an instrument's controls, click the little arrows beside each setting.

➤ To close an instrument, click its close box.

➤ To remove an instrument, drag its icon back to the instrument shelf.

➤ To change the color of a wire, double-click it and choose a color.

➤ To add information to a circuit, choose Description from the Window menu.

➤ To print, choose Print from the File menu.

Chapter 5
Trying Out the Digital Instruments

You can learn how to use Electronic Workbench's digital instruments in a short time by following the directions in this chapter for testing an RS flip-flop circuit.

If you've used Electronics Workbench to build analog circuits, you already know the basics of building digital circuits. What's different is a new set of components and test instruments. Simple instructions for using the mouse and menus are given as you go. If you want more information, see Chapter 2: User Interface.

Chapter 5
Trying Out the Digital Instruments

Testing a Circuit

In the previous two chapters, you have learned how to build and test a simple analog circuit. Now, in this tutorial, you will open the flip-flop circuit provided with Electronics Workbench and test it using the simulated test instruments. While each instrument has a different function, the way you use the instruments is similar. For this flip-flop circuit, you will use the word generator to supply input and the logic analyzer to display the signal.

➤ Choose Open from the File menu.

➤ If necessary, change to the Tutorial folder. Select RS Flip Flop from the list and choose Open or double-click RS Flip Flop to open it.

Trying Out the Word Generator

First, add a word generator to supply input to the flip-flop circuit. It sends a bit pattern into the circuit to make it operate.

Word generator icon

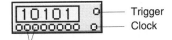

Trigger
Clock

Output terminals, one for each bit in an 8-bit word.

➤ To place the word generator on the workspace, point to its icon on the instrument shelf, press the mouse button, and drag.

➤ Connect its terminals as shown below. (Point to the leftmost terminal so it highlights, and drag a wire to connector S. Then connect the second terminal to R.)

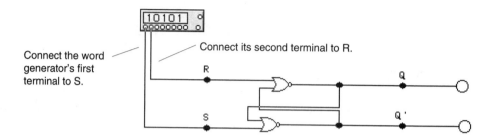

Connect the word generator's first terminal to S.

Connect its second terminal to R.

Opening the Word Generator

To set up the word generator, or any test instrument, it must be"zoomed open."

➤ To open an instrument's icon, select it and choose Zoom from the Circuit menu. Alternatively, double-click the instrument icon.

Change these bits to 1.

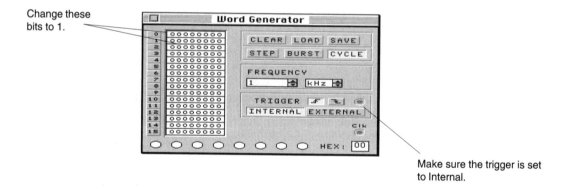

Make sure the trigger is set to Internal.

➤ To move an instrument, drag it by its title bar.

➤ To close an instrument, double-click its Control-menu box.

Entering Words in the Word Generator

On the word generator you'll see a number of buttons and a large field where you enter patterns of ones or zeros to form up to sixteen 8-bit words.

Since the RS flip-flop circuit you are building has two inputs, you only need to create a bit pattern in the word generator's first two columns.

Tip To test a circuit, use a bit pattern that gives you a predictable output, as indicated by a truth table.

➤ Enter the inputs S and R for the predicted outputs Q and Q′, as shown below.

Inputs		Outputs		
S	R	Q	Q′	
1	0	1	0	
0	0	1	0	(no change from previous state)
0	1	0	1	
0	0	0	1	(no change from previous state)
1	1	X	X	(undefined)

1. The first condition in the truth table is S = 1, R = 0, so click the first zero in the row 0 and type **1**.

2. In the third condition S = 0, R = 1, so click the second zero in row 2, and type **1** again.

The second and fourth conditions are zeros, so you don't have to change the word generator. The last condition is prohibited, since the outputs cannot be predicted.

Tip Once you have clicked a bit in the word generator, you can press the arrow keys to move the insertion point to other bits.

Change these
bits to 1.

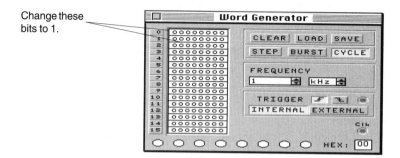

Activating a Circuit

➤ While watching the probes, click the Step button on the word generator three times to send the bits into the circuit. When the state changes, the alternate probe lights up.

Concept When Q = 1 and Q′ = 0, the flip-flop is in the set state (or 1-state) and the probe attached to Q lights up. When Q = 0 and Q′ = 1, the flip-flop is in the reset or clear state, and the probe attached to Q′ lights up.

Explore Try activating the circuit using the Burst and Cycle buttons. Clicking Burst sends a series of 16 words; clicking Cycle sends a continuous stream of words. To stop the simulation, turn off the power switch.

Tip You can also activate the circuit by clicking the power switch at the top of the screen or by choosing Activate from the Circuit menu. The Step, Burst or Cycle setting on the word generator determines whether the input is one word, a series of 16 words, or a continuous cycle.

Now you have the input to the circuit ready. The next step is to set up the logic analyzer so you can see the output.

Trying Out the Logic Analyzer

The eight-channel logic analyzer displays a circuit's output as a waveform diagram showing voltage level and timing, similar to what you might observe on an oscilloscope attached to an analog circuit.

Logic analyzer icon

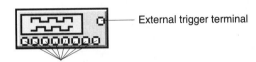

External trigger terminal

Eight input terminals

➤ Attach a logic analyzer to the flip-flop circuit as shown below. Connect the first terminal to connector S, the second terminal to R, the third terminal to Q and the fourth terminal to Q´.

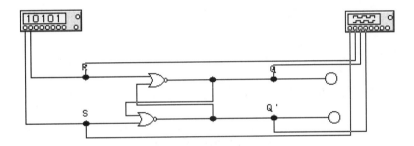

➤ Open the logic analyzer. (Either double-click it, or select it and choose Zoom from the Circuit menu.) If it covers the word generator or circuit, drag it out of the way.

➤ Activate the circuit by clicking the Cycle button on the word generator. You should see input and output signals similar to those shown below. (The signal starts with the currently highlighted word in the word generator.)

As the input signals change state, the output signals respond according to the truth table.

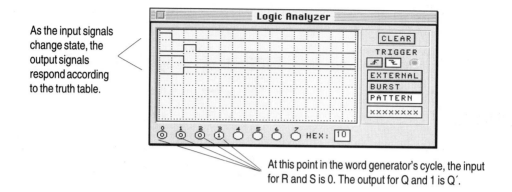

At this point in the word generator's cycle, the input for R and S is 0. The output for Q and 1 is Q´.

Help If you don't see similar signals, check the word patterns in the word generator, the settings on the word generator and logic analyzer, and the circuit wiring.

➤ Click the power switch or press ⌘-T to stop the simulation.

Changing the Color of Wires

If you have a color display, try making the wires going to each of the logic analyzer's terminals a different color. When the circuit is activated again, each signal will be the same color as its wire, so you can easily correlate input or output with the resulting waveform.

➤ To make a wire a different color, select it and choose Wire Color from the Circuit menu. Then choose the color you want from the dialog box that appears.

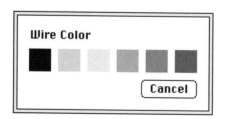

Tip You can also double-click a wire to change its color.

If your Macintosh cannot display colors, or if you have changed the Monitors control panel setting to Black & White or 4-color, the Wire Color command is dimmed.

➤ Save your work again by choosing Save from the File menu.

Trying Out Some More Features

Practice some of the things you've learned by building another circuit, this time using the logic converter to help you analyze and transform the circuit.

Starting a New Circuit

➤ To begin building a new circuit, choose New from the File menu. A new workspace will open. (If you have any unsaved changes in your current circuit, you will be asked to save them.)

➤ Start by creating a simple circuit using a NOT, an AND and an OR gate.

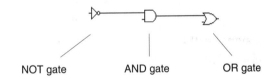

NOT gate   AND gate   OR gate

➤ You can modify the number of inputs for the gates by simply double clicking to open a dialog box. Use the pull-down menu to increase or decrease the number of inputs, then click Accept to accept the number, or Cancel to ignore the change.

Trying Out the Logic Converter

The logic converter can convert a digital circuit among different representations—truth table, Boolean expressions and circuit schematic.

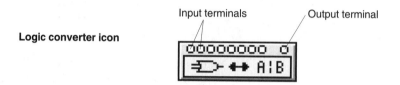

Logic converter icon

First, use it to generate a truth table for the circuit you just created.

➤ Drag the logic converter from the instrument shelf, and place it below the circuit. Then attach it to the circuit's inputs and output as shown.

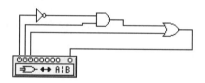

Deriving a Truth Table from a Circuit

➤ Open the logic converter by double-clicking it.

➤ Click the "Circuit to Truth Table" button.

The logic converter will calculate and display the circuit's truth table.

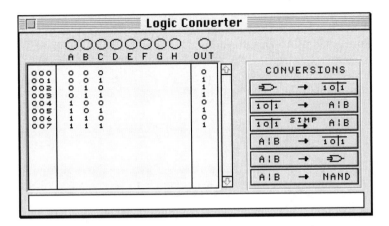

Converting a Truth Table to a Boolean Expression

Once you have a truth table, the logic converter can transform it into a Boolean function in the form of an algebraic expression.

➤ Click the "Truth Table to Boolean Expression" button.

The Boolean expression will be displayed at the bottom of the logic converter.

For this circuit the expression is $A'B'C + A'BC' + A'BC + AB'C + ABC$. Some expressions can be recalculated into a simpler form.

➤ To try to simplify the Boolean expression, click the "Simplify" button. In this case, the expression can be simplified to $A'B + C$.

Converting a Boolean Expression to a Circuit

The logic converter can also transform a Boolean expression into a circuit composed of AND, OR and/or NOT gates.

➤ To transform a Boolean expression into a circuit, click the "Boolean to Circuit" button.

The gates that fulfill the expression will appear, selected, on the workspace. (If necessary, move the logic converter to see them.) Point to one of the components, press and hold the mouse button, and drag the circuit to a clear area. Then click an empty spot on the workspace. You will see the circuit you began with, in a slightly different configuration.

Creating a Circuit from a Truth Table

Now try using the logic converter to enter a truth table, convert it to a Boolean expression, and then turn it into a circuit.

➤ Start a new circuit by choosing New from the File menu. (Save the other circuits first if you want.)

➤ Drag a logic converter to the workspace and open it.

➤ To create a truth table:

1. Click the number of inputs you want, from A up to H, at the top of the logic converter. The inputs are preset in a standard truth table format. (For example, click inputs for A, B, and C.)

2. The values in the output column are initially set to 0. Click the output values you want to change, and type a **1**. (For example, type the pattern shown below.)

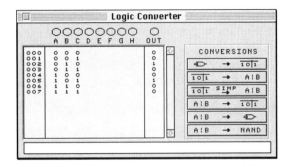

3. Click the "Simplify" button to convert the truth table to the simplest possible Boolean expression. (A´BC´ + AB´C)

4. Click the "Boolean to Circuit" button to create a circuit.

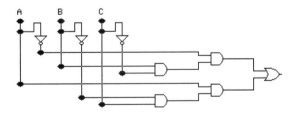

The resulting circuit will appear, selected, on the workspace. If you want to move it, point to one component and drag the circuit. Then click an empty spot on the workspace to deselect it.

➤ Close the logic converter by double-clicking its close box.

The Next Step

If you want to practice some of the things you've learned, try experimenting with the sample circuits included with Electronics Workbench.

➤ To open a sample circuit:

1. Choose Open from the File menu. A directory dialog box appears.

2. Open the "Samples" folder and choose a circuit. (If you want to look at simple digital circuits, you will find them in the "Simple Circuits" folder, within the "Samples" folder.)

3. Select a file from the list of sample circuits, then choose OK. (Double-clicking a file also opens it.)

If you need guidance as you experiment, use the summary that follows, or refer to the more detailed information in the Electronics Workbench User's Reference. (To preserve the samples in their original form, use the Save As command in the File menu to save any changes you make.)

➤ If you are ready to leave Electronics Workbench, choose Quit from the File menu.

Summary

➤ To use a component, drag it from the parts bin to the workspace.

➤ To remove a component, drag it back to the parts bin.

➤ To select a component, point to it and click the mouse button. Shift-click to select additional components.

➤ To use a test instrument, drag its icon from the instrument shelf to the workspace. To remove an instrument, drag its icon back to the instrument shelf.

➤ Attach a test instrument to components in the circuit by dragging wires from its icon's terminals.

➤ Double-click an instrument icon to zoom it open.

➤ To activate a circuit, click the Step, Burst or Cycle buttons on the word generator, or click the power switch. To turn off the power, click the power switch.

➤ To change the color of a wire, double-click it and choose a color.

➤ To modify the number of inputs for a gate, double-click it and click on the arrows in the dialog box to increase or decrease the number.

➤ When you are finished, choose Quit from the File menu.

Reference

Chapter 6
Menu Reference

The Menu Reference chapter describes how to use each of Electronics Workbench's menu commands. It is organized according to the order in which menus and their commands appear, from left to right and from top to bottom. (A listing of menus and keyboard shortcuts is included on the Quick Reference Card.)

Chapter 6
Menu Reference

File Menu

The File menu contains commands you use to manage circuit files created with Electronics Workbench.

File	
New	⌘N
Open...	⌘O
Close	⌘W
Save	⌘S
Save As...	
Revert	
Page Setup...	
Print...	⌘P
Quit	⌘Q

File➤New   ⌘-N

Choose New to start a new circuit. If you've made changes to the current circuit, you will be asked if you want to save the circuit before it is closed. Then you'll see a new, untitled workspace.

When you start Electronics Workbench, a new circuit is opened automatically.

Tip When you open a new circuit, the contents of the Custom parts bin are determined by the default circuit Default. If you would like to modify the default circuits, see "Customizing the Workspace and Parts Bin for All Circuits" in Chapter 2: User Interface.

File➤Open   ⌘-o

Use the Open command to open previously created circuit files.

➤ To open a file:

1. Choose Open from the File menu. You'll see a directory dialog box.

Current directory

Select the circuit
you want to open.
(As a shortcut,
double-click the
circuit name.)

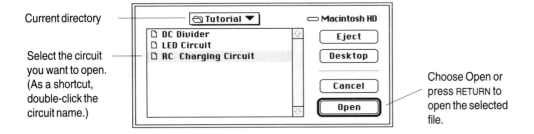

Choose Open or
press RETURN to
open the selected
file.

2. If necessary, change to the disk or folder that contains the file you
    want.

3. Select the circuit name from the Files list box and choose Open. Or
    double-click the circuit name to open the circuit.

For more information, see "Using Dialog Boxes" in Chapter 2: User
Interface.

For information about opening circuits created with an earlier version of
Electronics Workbench, see Appendix A. For information on opening
circuits created on a PC, see Appendix B.

File➤Close   ⌘-w

Use the Close command to close the active window.

The circuit and parts bin windows cannot be closed. If either of these is the
active window, the close command is dimmed. (The circuit closes
automatically when you open a new circuit or quit Electronics Workbench.
The parts bin window can be hidden, if desired, using the Restrictions
command in the Circuit menu.)

Tip You can close all Help windows at once by choosing Close Help Windows from the Help menu.

File➤Save   ⌘-s

The Save command saves the current circuit. You use the Save command to save both new and existing circuits.

➤ To save a new, untitled circuit:

1. Choose Save from the File menu. You'll see a directory dialog box.

2. If you want, change to a different folder or disk.

3. Type a name for the circuit in the text box.

4. Choose OK.

Using a dialog box is described more fully in Chapter 2: User Interface.

➤ To save an existing circuit, choose Save from the File menu. Changes you have made since you opened or saved the circuit will be stored.

It is a good idea to save frequently. If the power goes off, you will lose only work done since you last saved. Plus, you can then undo changes made to a circuit since it was last saved using the Revert To Saved command, described on the next page.

Tip If you want to preserve the original circuit without changes, choose Save As instead of Save.

Tip If you plan to transfer circuits between the Macintosh and a PC, you can simplify the process by giving your circuits DOS names. A DOS name is composed of up to eight characters, with no spaces. Add a .CA4 filename extension to circuit names. For more information, see Appendix B: Sharing circuits with PCs.

File➤Save As

Use the Save As command to make a copy of the current circuit and save it with a new filename. The original circuit closes, and the newly named circuit remains open.

Tip Use the Save As command to experiment safely on a copy of a circuit, without changing the original.

File➤Revert

Choose Revert to restore a circuit to the way it was when you last saved. You can think of this command as a form of "undo."

File➤Page Setup

If you want to change paper size, circuit orientation or other print options, or if you change the printer specified in the Chooser, choose Page Setup from the File menu.

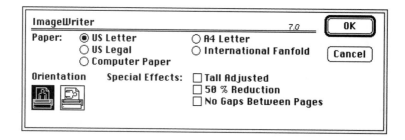

The options in the Page Setup dialog box depend on the printer that is selected in the Chooser.

File➤Print   ⌘-P

You can print a circuit, its description, parts list and analysis options, as well as any instruments or subcircuits used.

➤ To print:

1. Choose Print from the File menu. A dialog box appears.

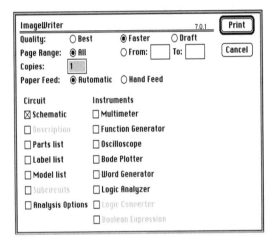

2. Select the items you want printed so an X appears beside them. To deselect an item, click it again. (Dimmed items are not used in the current circuit and cannot be selected.)

3. Choose Print.

File➤Quit   ⌘-Q

Choose Quit to close the current circuit and leave Electronics Workbench. If you have unsaved changes, you will be asked if you want to save the circuit.

Edit Menu

The Edit menu contains commands that can be used to remove, duplicate or select information. The Cut, Copy, Paste and Delete commands act on selected text, components and subcircuit icons. If you haven't selected a component, these commands are dimmed. (For directions on selecting, see Chapter 2: User Interface.)

```
┌─────────────────────┐
│ Edit                │
│ Undo          ⌘Z    │
├─────────────────────┤
│ Cut           ⌘H    │
│ Copy          ⌘C    │
│ Paste         ⌘U    │
│ Delete              │
│ Select All    ⌘A    │
├─────────────────────┤
│ Show Clipboard      │
└─────────────────────┘
```

Edit➤Undo   ⌘-Z

The Undo command is always dimmed. (If you want to undo all changes made since you opened or saved the current cicuit, choose Revert from the file menu.)

Edit➤Cut   ⌘-X

Use the Cut command to remove selected components, circuits or text. What you cut is placed on the Clipboard so you can paste it elsewhere.

Instrument icons cannot be cut. To remove an instrument icon from a circuit, drag it back to the instrument shelf.

Edit➤Copy   ⌘-C

Copy makes a copy of selected components, circuits or text. The copy is placed on the Clipboard. You can then use the Paste command to paste the copy elsewhere. Instrument icons cannot be copied.

Caution

Whatever is on the Clipboard is replaced when a new selection is cut or copied. If you want to delete an object permanently, without losing the contents of the Clipboard, use the Delete command.

Edit➤Paste   ⌘-V

Paste replicates the contents of the Clipboard and places the copy in the active window. Using the Paste command does not affect the contents of the Clipboard.

The contents of the Clipboard might be components or text. The information on the Clipboard can only be pasted into locations that can contain similar information. For example, you cannot paste a component into the description window.

Pasting Components into the Custom Parts Bin

If you have cut or deleted a component from the custom parts bin, you can replace it using the Paste command.

➤ To specify the location in which a component will be pasted, select the component you want it to follow. Then choose Paste. If no component is selected, the component will be placed at the bottom of the parts bin.

Pasting Text from Another Application

Text copied onto the Clipboard from another application can be pasted into the description window. If the text was previously formatted, its formatting will be removed. Graphics from another application cannot be pasted into Electronics Workbench.

Edit➤Delete

Choose Delete if you want to remove selected components or text permanently. The Delete command does not place the selection on the Clipboard and does not affect anything currently on the Clipboard.

Caution

Use the Delete command with care. Deleted information cannot be retrieved.

Edit➤Select All

The Select All command selects all information in the active window.

For example, if the circuit window is active, choosing Select All selects all components and instrument icons on the circuit's workspace, so you can easily perform an action such as moving or copying. If a subcircuit is active, choosing Select All selects everything in the subcircuit's workspace. If the description window is active, choosing Select All selects all text in the window.

Tip If you want to select all but a few components and instruments, use the Select All command and then deselect the ones you don't want by shift-clicking.

For directions on selecting with a mouse, see "Selecting" in Chapter 2: User Interface.

Edit➤Show Clipboard

The Clipboard is a temporary storage location for components or text you want to place elsewhere in a circuit. You can also use the Clipboard to transfer information from Electronics Workbench to another application.

When you select information in Electronics Workbench and then use the Cut or Copy command, your selection is placed on the Clipboard. Anything previously on the Clipboard is deleted. When you choose Paste, Electronics Workbench replicates the information on the Clipboard and places it in the active window.

The Clipboard can hold both graphics (components or circuits) and text. If the active window cannot hold the type of information that is on the Clipboard, or if the Clipboard is empty, the Paste command cannot be chosen. For example, if the Clipboard contains components, and a text insertion point is selected in the description window, the Paste command is dimmed.

➤ To see the Clipboard, choose Show Clipboard from the Edit menu.

To close the Clipboard, click its close box.

Circuit Menu

The Circuit menu contains commands that you use to create and test a circuit.

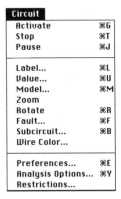

Circuit➤Activate   ⌘-G

The Activate command has the same effect as turning on the power switch in the top right corner of the display. Activating a circuit starts a sequence of mathematical operations to compute values for the test points in the circuit.

➤ To activate a circuit, choose Activate from the Circuit menu, or click the power switch. The power switch remains turned on (at "1") until the simulation is finished and final values are displayed on the test instruments attached to the circuit.

Tip You can also activate a digital circuit from the word generator.

Creating Test Points

Before you activate a circuit, create test points on nodes whose values you want to measure. (A node is a set of points formed by the connection of two or more components.)

➤ To create a test point, insert a connector into a wire joining two or more components. Then attach an instrument to the test point.

During Simulation

When you activate a circuit, Electronics Workbench begins to simulate the circuit's behavior. The method used for simulation depends on the circuit's construction, the instruments attached to the circuit, and the options specified in the Analysis Options dialog box. During simulation, a status indicator appears beside the power switch to indicate the simulation's progress or state. The status indicator message for analog circuits depends on the type of analysis being carried out, as shown in the table on the next page.

For digital circuits, the status indicator message reflects the word generator setting: Step, Burst or Cycle. If the simulation is paused or stopped, or if an error occurs, a corresponding message appears.

If you are interested in an explanation of the methods used for circuit analysis, see the Analog Simulation Explanation in the Electronics Workbench Technical Reference.

Status Indicator Messages for Analog Circuits		
For analog circuits using...	The message during simulation is ...	The message after simulation is ...
Transient analysis	time: eg., "10.00 ms"	"Steady State"
Steady-state analysis (for linear circuits)	"DC Analysis" then "AC Analysis"	"Steady State"
Steady-state analysis (for nonlinear circuits)	"DC Analysis" then time; e.g., "10.00 ms"	"Steady State"
Bode plotter	"DC Analysis" then frequency; e.g., "10.00 mHz"	"Bode"

Making Changes During Simulation

You can make changes to a circuit while it is activated. For example, you can move components or windows, adjust the time base on the oscilloscope, or change the frequency of the function generator. If you make a change that invalidates the simulation (for example, by adding a component, changing a value, or changing the analysis type), the simulation is restarted automatically.

After Simulation is Completed

When a circuit's behavior has been computed, the power switch turns off and test instruments display their final results. At this point, you can move the instruments' probes to different test points in the circuit to test their values. (If you move the ammeter or Bode plotter, however, the circuit should be re-activated.)

If you create new test points or change the circuit's electrical composition, activate the circuit again to get new readings.

Circuit➤Stop   ⌘-T

Circuit simulation stops automatically when the circuit reaches steady state if steady state can be detected. You can stop a simulation yourself using the Stop command. Clicking the power switch also stops a simulation.

Tip An oscillating or switch-controlled circuit is unlikely to reach steady state. Use the Stop command to stop its simulation once you have seen enough of its behavior.

Tip If you want to include general information about a circuit, enter it in the description window, available from the Window menu.

Circuit➤Pause/Resume   ⌘-J

You can interrupt a simulation temporarily using the Pause command.
Pausing is useful if you want to take a longer look at a waveform or make
changes to an instrument setting. (The simulation of simple circuits may be
too quick to pause.)

To continue a paused simulation, choose Resume from the Circuit menu or
press ⌘-J.

Tip You can pause the oscilloscope automatically by turning on "Pause
after each screen" in the Analysis Options dialog box.

Circuit➤Label   ⌘-L

Use the Label command to label components in a circuit. Labels can make
a circuit more understandable. They are particularly useful if you want to
refer to points in a circuit in a description or set of instructions.

➤   To label a component:

1.   Select a component and choose Label from the Circuit menu.
     (Components without values or models can be double-clicked.)

2.   Type a label in the dialog box that appears. A label can be composed of
     any characters, including spaces.

3.   Choose OK.

The label should appear beside the component. If it doesn't appear, choose
Preferences from the Circuit menu and turn on "Show labels."

If you rotate a component, its label may rotate too. If a wire runs through a
label, you can shift the label to the right by adding several spaces before it
in the Label dialog box.

Circuit➤Value

⌘-U

Use the Value command to change the setting of simple components (such as resistors, capacitors and switches). Values can be changed while components are in the parts bin or on the workspace. You can also use the Value command to control the internal resistance of the voltmeter and ammeter and set their mode to AC or DC.

➤ To change a component's value:

1. Select the component and choose Value from the Circuit menu. Or double-click the component. A dialog box appears.

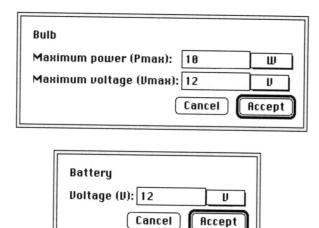

2. Type in a new value (or values).

3. If necessary, change the units by clicking the current units and choosing new units from the pop-up menu.

4. Choose Accept.

The value should appear near the component. If it doesn't, choose Preferences from the Circuit menu and turn on "Show values."

General Comments about Label, Value and Model

- Only one component can be labeled at a time. If more than one component is selected, or if no component is selected, the Label command is dimmed.

- The value or model of multiple copies of the same component can be set at once.

- An analog component has either a value or a model, not both. When you select an analog component, the command that does not apply is dimmed in the Circuit menu.

- Double-clicking a component to set its value or model is a good shortcut since it produces the dialog box appropriate for the component. If the component you double-click doesn't have a value or model, its Label box appears.

- If you rotate a component, its label, value or model may rotate also.

- You can control whether or not labels, values or models are displayed on the workspace using the Preferences command in the Circuit menu.

- You can set a component's label, value or model from either the workspace or the parts bin. Changes you make to a component on the workspace affect only that component. Changes you make to a component in the parts bin affect all copies you subsequently place on the workspace *for the current circuit only*. (To change the parts bin for all new circuits, see "Customizing the Workspace and Parts Bin for All New Circuits" in Chapter 2: User Interface.)

Circuit➤Model ⌘-M

The Model command is available when using complex analog components (such as a transistor or diode) or digital components.

Component models are preset to Ideal. An ideal model is a close approximation of the real component, with most parameters set to 0 or infinity. This allows Electronics Workbench to quickly simulate the component's behavior.

For most circuit simulations, the preset ideal models are all you need. If you want to increase the accuracy of your test results, use the Model command to choose a real-world model from the default libraries supplied with Electronics Workbench, or create your own models.

Using a Model Supplied with Electronics Workbench

➤ To choose a component model:

1. Select the component and choose Model from the Circuit menu. Or double-click the component. A dialog box appears.

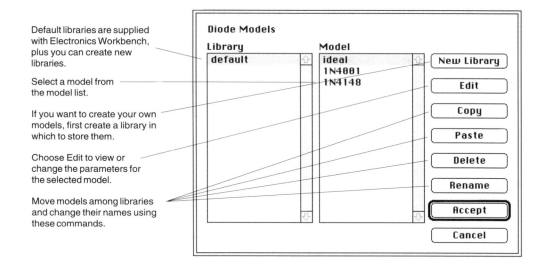

Default libraries are supplied with Electronics Workbench, plus you can create new libraries.

Select a model from the model list.

If you want to create your own models, first create a library in which to store them.

Choose Edit to view or change the parameters for the selected model.

Move models among libraries and change their names using these commands.

Diode Models

Library
default

Model
ideal
1N4001
1N4148

New Library

Edit

Copy

Paste

Delete

Rename

Accept

Cancel

2. Select a new model from the Model list. Then choose Accept. (Or double-click the model name.)

You can control whether or not the model name appears on the workspace using the Preferences command in the Circuit menu.

About SPICE

Component models are based on industry-standard SPICE algorithms. SPICE is an acronym for Simulation Program with Integrated Circuit Emphasis, a general-purpose circuit-simulation program developed at the University of California, Berkley. If you are not familiar with SPICE, restrict yourself to using the models supplied with Electronics Workbench. (If you want to learn more about SPICE modeling, see "Readings about SPICE" in the Electronics Workbench Technical Reference.)

Creating New Libraries and Models

If you are familiar with SPICE modeling and want to use component models that are not included in the default model libraries, you can create new models. The first step is to create a new library in which to store your models. (Changing models in a default library is not recommended.)

➤ To create a library in which to store your own models, choose New Library from the Model dialog box. Then type a name in the box that appears, and choose OK.

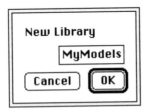

Creating a library creates a file of the same name. A library name can have no more than eight characters including letters, numbers and underscores. Each component's library files are given a unique filename extension that differentiates them from other components' library files.

➤ To create a new model:

1. Make a copy of a similar model in the default library by selecting it in the model list and choosing Copy.

2. Select the library you want to store your model in.

3. Choose Paste. A dialog box will appear in which you can type a new name for the model. (Model names should not include spaces.) Then choose OK. The model is pasted into your library.

4. To make changes to the copied model, select it (if it is not already selected), and choose Edit. You will see a dialog box listing the model's parameters.

Diode Model 'INI4'

Saturation current (Is):	1e-14	A
Ohmic resistance (rs):	0	Ω
Zero-bias junction capacitance (Cj):	0	F
Junction potential (Ù):	0.75	U
Transit time (ι):	0	s
Junction grading coefficient (m):	0	

[Cancel] [[Accept]]

---

5. Select the parameters you want to change, and type new ones. Then choose Accept.

See the Analog Simulation Explanation in the Electronics Workbench Technical Reference for a description of the parameters used for component models.

Saving Models and Libraries

When you save a circuit, any changes you have made to models are saved with the circuit. You will also be asked if you want to save changes made to your model library. Choose Yes, so that models in the library will correspond with models in the circuit.

If you do not save changes to a model library, the next time you open a circuit that uses models from it you will be asked if you want to keep the circuit's models or use the library's models. (If the library can't be found, you'll be asked if you want to use the models in the default library.) If you are unsure of what to do, it is safer to keep the circuit's models and create a new library in which to store them.

Caution

Model libraries are placed in the Models folder. If a model library is moved from the Models folder, or if the Models folder is moved out of the Electronics Workbench folder, circuit models will not be found.

Tip If you have proliferating copies of similar models, perhaps spread over several libraries, take time to do some housekeeping. Use the Delete button on the Model dialog box to remove extra copies and, if necessary, use the Rename button to create meaningful model names.

Models and Network Use If your license agreement permits network use by more than one user, you may want to limit access to the models folder. For example, you could allow everyone to see the Models folder and its files, but allow only specified users or groups to make changes.

Circuit➤Zoom   ⌘-Z

Use the Zoom command to open a selected instrument or subcircuit icon. Zoom works whether the icon is on the workspace, on the instrument shelf or in the parts bin.

➤   To open a test instrument or subcircuit icon, select it and choose Zoom from the Circuit menu. Double-clicking the icon has the same effect as choosing Zoom.

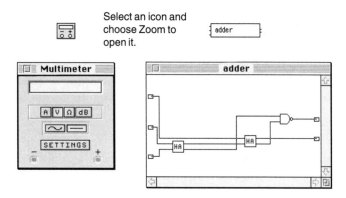

Select an icon and choose Zoom to open it.

Tip If an instrument or subcircuit is already zoomed open, selecting its icon and choosing Zoom brings its window to the front.

Circuit➤Rotate   ⌘-R

The Rotate command rotates the selected component or components 90 degrees clockwise. A component's label and value or model (if displayed) may rotate along with the component. Wires attached to the component are rerouted automatically.

Exceptions When you rotate the ammeter and voltmeter, only their terminals rotate. When you rotate a transistor, it sometimes "flips" or reverses symmetry so you can follow standard drafting conventions. Subcircuit icons cannot be rotated.

Circuit➤Subcircuit   ⌘-B

Use the Subcircuit command to combine all or part of a circuit into a subcircuit in effect creating your own integrated circuit. When you create a subcircuit, the selected components are placed on a new workspace, which is displayed in a window in the center of the circuit workspace. A corresponding subcircuit icon (a labeled rectangle) is placed automatically at the bottom of the parts bin *for the current circuit only.*

➤ To create a subcircuit:

1. Select the components you want in the subcircuit.

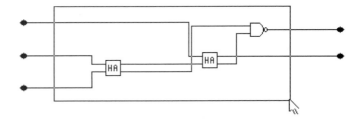

A subcircuit can have as many components as you want. Any wires leading to other components or connectors in the circuit will become terminals on the subcircuit icon.

2. Choose Subcircuit from the Circuit menu. You'll see a dialog box.

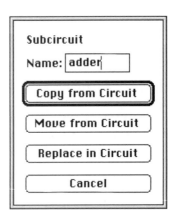

3. Type a name for the subcircuit.

4. Choose what you want to happen to the selected components when the subcircuit is created.

•   "Copy from Circuit" places a copy of the selected components in the subcircuit. The original components remain as they are on the workspace.

•   "Move from Circuit" removes the selected components from the circuit so they appear only in the subcircuit.

•   "Replace in Circuit" places the selected components in the subcircuit and wires the new subcircuit icon into the circuit.

Using a Subcircuit

A subcircuit has two views: a rectangular subcircuit icon and a "zoomed-open" view of the components in the subcircuit. Terminals appear on the subcircuit icon wherever wires leave the subcircuit's workspace.

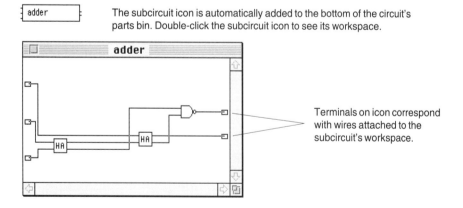

The subcircuit icon is automatically added to the bottom of the circuit's parts bin. Double-click the subcircuit icon to see its workspace.

Terminals on icon correspond with wires attached to the subcircuit's workspace.

➤   To add a subcircuit to a circuit, drag its icon from the parts bin to the workspace. Drag wires from its terminals to make connections.

➤   To open a subcircuit icon, select it and choose Zoom from the Circuit menu. Or double-click the icon. (The subcircuit icon can be opened from either the workspace or parts bin.)

A subcircuit is displayed in a window that you can move, scroll and resize like other windows. When the subcircuit window is open, you can edit it. For example, you could add or delete a component or create a new terminal. A change made to one copy of a subcircuit affects all other copies of the subcircuit in the circuit in which you are working.

➤ To create a new terminal for a subcircuit, drag a wire from a component in the subcircuit to an edge of the subcircuit window. When a small box appears, release the mouse button. A subcircuit can have an unlimited number of terminals on each of its four sides.

➤ If a subcircuit becomes covered, choose Bring Subcircuits to Front from the Window menu, or click its title bar.

Using a Subcircuit in Other Circuits

A subcircuit is saved with its circuit, but is not automatically added to the parts bin for all circuits. You can add a subcircuit to other circuits using one of two methods:

• Copy the subcircuit icon and paste it into another circuit using the Copy and Paste commands.

• If you want a subcircuit to appear in the parts bins for all new circuits, add it to the Default circuit in the EWB Files folder.

Circuit➤Wire Color

When you wire a circuit, the wires are black. If your Macintosh can display colors, you can change the color of wires using the Wire Color command. Coloring wires makes them easier to distinguish. Using different colors is particularly helpful in identifying waveforms on the oscilloscope and logic analyzer, since they are the same color as their probes.

➤ To change the color of a wire, select it and choose Wire Color from the Circuit menu. Or double-click the wire. Then choose a color from the dialog box that appears.

If your Macintosh cannot display colors, or if the Macintosh control panel is set to black and white or 4-color, the Wire Color command is dimmed.

Circuit➤Preferences

⌘-E

Use the Preferences command to control display options for the current circuit. You can specify whether you want to show or hide a workspace grid or turn it off altogether; plus you can show or hide component labels.

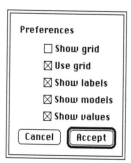

The default preferences are shown above. Changes you make to the preferences affect only the current circuit.

Using the grid makes it more likely that circuit wires will be straight. When a component is added to the workspace, its terminals are lined up with a grid point, even if the grid is not showing.

Circuit➤Analysis Options   ⌘-Y

The method used to simulate circuit behavior depends on the components
and instruments used in a circuit and the analysis options specified in the
Analysis Options dialog box.

➤   To specify how a circuit is analyzed, choose Analysis Options from the
    Circuit menu. You'll see the Analysis Options dialog box, with the default
    settings shown below.

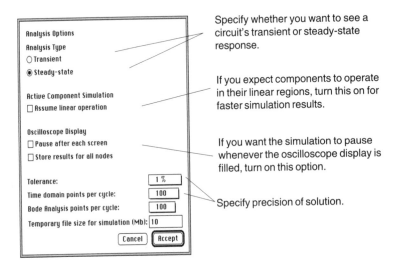

Analysis Options

Analysis Type
○ Transient
◉ Steady-state

Active Component Simulation
☐ Assume linear operation

Oscilloscope Display
☐ Pause after each screen
☐ Store results for all nodes

Tolerance: `1 %`
Time domain points per cycle: `100`
Bode Analysis points per cycle: `100`
Temporary file size for simulation (Mb): `10`

[Cancel] [Accept]

Specify whether you want to see a
circuit's transient or steady-state
response.

If you expect components to operate
in their linear regions, turn this on for
faster simulation results.

If you want the simulation to pause
whenever the oscilloscope display is
filled, turn on this option.

Specify precision of solution.

There is no need to change the default analysis options unless you 1) are
interested in a circuit's transient state, 2) have a linear circuit and want
the quickest possible simulation, or 3) want an exacting level of precision.

While the settings in the Analysis Options dialog box can affect interim
values displayed on the multimeter, voltmeter and ammeter, for the most
part it is the way they affect the output displayed on the oscilloscope that is
of interest. (The analysis options settings have no effect on the Bode
plotter, which always does an AC frequency-response analysis.)

If you are interested in a detailed explanation of the analyses used by
Electronics Workbench, and how they relate to SPICE, see the Electronics
Workbench Technical Reference Simulation Explanation.

Transient Analysis

Select "Transient" analysis to force initial conditions for each component to zero so that you can analyze the circuit's behavior when the power is first turned on. For example, use transient analysis to see a circuit's charging curve or oscillations.

Tip Another way to see a transient response is to include a switch in the circuit. When you close a switch, circuit simulation starts with zero initial conditions.

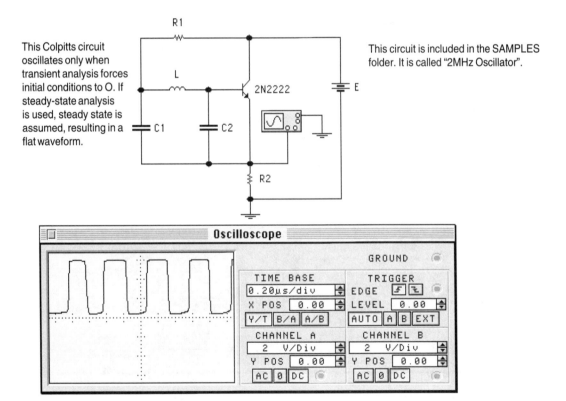

This Colpitts circuit oscillates only when transient analysis forces initial conditions to O. If steady-state analysis is used, steady state is assumed, resulting in a flat waveform.

This circuit is included in the SAMPLES folder. It is called "2MHz Oscillator".

Steady-State Analysis

Select "Steady-state" analysis to see a circuit's response once steady state
has been reached. Initial conditions for each component are determined by
its DC operating point, found through DC analysis.

When "Steady-state" is selected, you can also specify whether or not
Electronics Workbench should "Assume linear operation" for the circuit, as
described on the next page.

This circuit, tested using steady-state analysis,
is biased deliberately to show output distortion. If
the circuit is simulated with "Assume linear
operation" selected, it gives an incorrect result
without clipping or distortion.

This circuit is included in
the "Samples" folder. It is
called "Common Emitter
Amp".

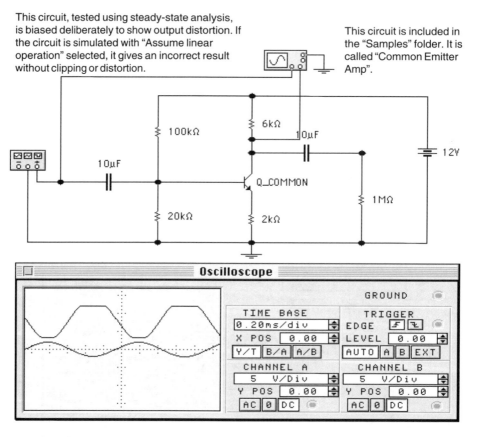

Tip The DC operating point is also known as the Q (for "quiescent") point.
It is the point at which the voltage and current of the source are the same
as the voltage across, and the current into, the load. In other words, the
output voltage is ideally a linear reproduction of the input. The DC
operating point is necessary for SPICE simulations and the analysis
performed by Electronics Workbench, but it is not given as part of the
solution. You can find the DC operating point manually by doing a load-

Assume Linear Operation

If you want to see the steady-state response of a circuit composed of linear components such as resistors and sources, you can get simulation results more quickly by turning on "Assume linear operation." For circuits that include nonlinear components such as diodes or transistors, simulation results will be accurate only if the components are operating in their linear regions. (If Electronics Workbench can predict that assuming linear operation will not give accurate results, it will do a more detailed analysis automatically.)

The opamp in this first-order high pass filter (as in all filters) operates in its linear region, so you can get quick results by turning on "Assume linear operation."

This circuit, called "1 Pole Hi-Pass Filter", is included in the "Samples" folder.

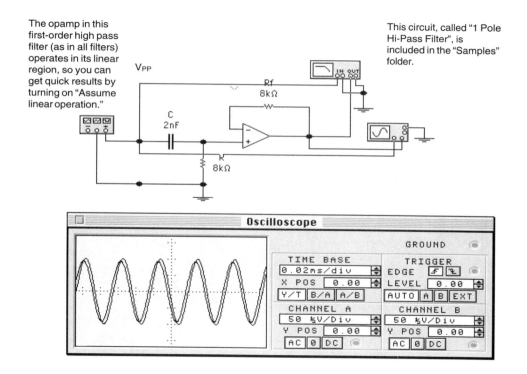

Tip Since nonlinear components sometimes operate in a linear region, you can try turning on "Assume linear operation" for circuits that include nonlinear components. If the results aren't what you expect, turn off "Assume linear operation," and re-activate the circuit.

Oscilloscope Display (Pause or Continuous)

The oscilloscope continues to display waveforms until the simulation is completed or steady state is reached. If you want time to analyze the waveforms, turn on "Pause after each screen" in the Analysis Options dialog box. When the circuit is activated, the simulation will pause once the waveforms reach the right edge of the oscilloscope. To continue the simulation, press ⌘-J or choose Resume from the Circuit menu.

Tip You can also use the Pause command in the Circuit menu to interrupt the drawing of waveforms at any point on the oscilloscope display.

Tolerance (10%-1e-9%)

Tolerance is a measurement of precision in the solution for a circuit. To simulate the behavior of a circuit, Electronics Workbench performs a series of computations to converge on a solution. The value of one computation is compared with the previous value. Simulation continues until two successive values are within the specified degree of tolerance. Tolerance is preset to 1%, which means that a result within one percent of the preceding result is considered acceptable, and simulation stops. For example, if $V_i = 100$ on one pass and $V_i = 101$ on the next pass, then $V = 101$ is given as the solution because it is within a tolerance of 1%. However, if the tolerance is set to 1e-6%, then the simulation would continue until a more precise solution of, for example, 100.000005, was reached. ("e" means exponential; 1e-3% is 0.001%)

Tolerance:	10 %
	1 %
	0.1 %
	0.01 %
	1e-3 %
	1e-4 %
	1e-5 %
	1e-6 %
	1e-7 %
	1e-8 %
	1e-9 %

➤ To change the tolerance, click the current setting and choose a new setting from the menu that appears.

Tip Reducing the tolerance increases the time needed to simulate a circuit's behavior. Use a 1% tolerance where possible. If you see a message saying that Electronics Workbench can't reach a solution, increase the tolerance to 1% or 10%, and activate the circuit again. \

Points per Cycle (50-1000)

The length of the cycle used in analysis is determined by the lowest-frequency source in the circuit (except when using the Bode plotter, which generates its own frequencies). A frequency setting of 1 Hz generates one cycle per second. A 1 kHz setting generates 1000 cycles per second.

By default, 100 points in each cycle are analyzed. If you need a more precise solution, you can increase the number of points per cycle by multiples of 100 up to 1000. For example, if the oscilloscope displays a triangular wave instead of the sine wave you were expecting, it may be that not enough points in the cycle were analyzed. Increasing the number of points per cycle in such a case may produce a smoother waveform.

Bode Analysis points per cycle (50-1000)

By default, 100 points are analyzed for a Bode plot. If you need a more precise solution, you can increase the number of points per cycle.

➤ To change the number of points per cycle, click the present setting and choose a new setting from the menu that appears.

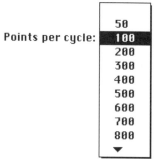

Tip Increasing the number of points per cycle also increases the time needed to simulate a circuit. Use the preset value, 100 points per cycle, whenever possible.

If a solution cannot be reached during simulation, lower the points per cycle to 50 or 100, and activate the circuit again.

Window Menu

Use commands in the Window menu to bring windows to the front and to arrange the layout of windows.

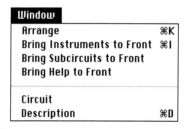

Window➤Arrange   ⌘-K

Choose Arrange to neatly organize the workspace and parts bin windows, as well as the description window if it is open. The way these windows will be arranged depends on their current positions. For example, if you have placed the parts bin to the left of the workspace and the description window above the workspace, choosing Arrange neatly adjusts their position so they are as big as possible without overlapping.

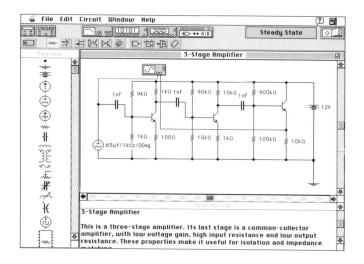

Tip Rearranging windows affects only the present circuit. If you want to change the position of these windows for all circuits, change the default circuits. For more information, see "Customizing the Workspace and Parts Bin" in Chapter 1: Getting Started.

Window▶Bring Instruments to Front   ⌘-I

Choose Bring Instruments to Front from the Window menu to bring all open instruments to the front. If instruments obscure each other, click the title bar of the one you want to see, or drag to rearrange them.

Window➤Bring Subciruits to Front

Choose Bring Subcircuits to Front from the Window menu to bring all open subcircuit workspaces to the front.

Window➤Bring Help to Front

Choosing Bring Help to Front brings all open Help windows to the front.

Window➤Circuit

Choose Circuit from the Window menu to bring the circuit's workspacewindow to the front.

Window➤Description   ⌘-D

Choose Description from the Window menu to open the description window. (If the description window is already open, choosing Description brings it to the front.) You can type comments or directions in the description window, or paste text from another application or circuit description.

Options for Displaying the Description Window

When you first open the description window, it is displayed at the bottom of the workspace, possibly covering part of the circuit. You can make the window smaller by dragging its size box. If you want text displayed along with the circuit, choose Arrange from the Window menu to reposition and resize the workspace and description windows so they can be displayed simultaneously.

Help Menu

Use the Help menu to get on-screen information. You can get details about a specific component or instrument, a table of contents for general browsing, and an index of topics in the Help system.

Help➤Help   ⌘-?

➤ To get information about a component or instrument icon, select it and choose Help from the Help menu.

➤ To go to the Help table of contents, make sure nothing is selected, and choose Help from the Help menu. (If there is something selected, click an empty spot on the workspace to deselect it before choosing Help.)

Here is an example Help window.

Double-click the Control-menu box to close the window.

Choose highlighted text for more information.

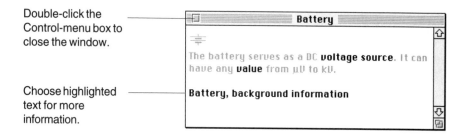

➤   To get more information, choose highlighted text.

➤   To close a Help window, click its close box. Or choose Close Help Windows from the Help menu. (Choosing Close Help Windows closes all open Help windows, not just the active window.)

Help➤Help Index

Choosing Help Index from the Help menu displays an index of Help topics. Choose an entry for information.

Tip If you are looking up a number of topics, drag the Help Index window to one corner of the screen so it is not obscured as other Help windows are displayed.

Help➤Close Help Windows   ⌘-H

Use the Close Help Windows command to close all open Help windows.

Appendices

Appendix A
For Users of Earlier Versions

What's New in Version 4.0

Functional Changes

You can use a single workspace to build both analog and digital circuits. You now run Electronics Workbench with a single command, regardless of what kind of circuit you plan to build. All circuits, regardless of their type, have the file type CA4.

The single parts bin has been divided into a number of smaller, separate bins, organized by component type. As a result, to display the parts bin containing the components you want to use, you need to click on a parts bin button first.

The connector is now created automatically. You no longer need to manually add connectors. Electronics Workbench automatically adds them when you connect two wires.

Other Changes

- The original manual has been divided into two separate volumes. See the Preface for details.

- The Oscilloscope now has a Zoom button that gives you a more in-depth view of your circuit's output.

- You can now modify the number of inputs for gates.

- A new source has been added: 5-volt TTL

- New linear components have been added: potentiometer (variable resistor), variable capacitor and variable inductor.

- A centre-tap has been added to the transformer for use in centre-tapped configuration.

- New non-linear components have been added: bridge rectifier, Shockley diode, silicon-controlled rectifier (SCR), triac, diac, and 5-terminal opamp.

- New gates have been added: XNOR, tristate buffer and buffer.

- New combinational devices have been added: full adder, 3-to-8 decoder, 8-to-3 priority encoder, BCD-to-seven-segment decoder, 1-of-8 multiplexer and demultiplexer.

- Sequential devices have been added: RS flip-flop, JK flip-flop, JK flip-flop with active-low asynchronous inputs, D flip-flop, D flip-flop with active-low asynchronous inputs, counter and four-bit shift register.

- Hybrid components have been added: digital-to-analog converter (DAC),analog-to-digital converter (ADC), 555 timer, monostable multivibrator.

- Multiple frequencies are now supported.

Using Circuits Created with Earlier Versions

Opening Files Created with an Earlier Version of Electronics Workbench

You can use the Open command in the File menu to open files created with an earlier version of Electronics Workbench (files with type CA or CD for analog and digital files respectively). If you save the file, the type will be changed to CA4. The new file can be opened only with Electronics Workbench version 4.

About Parts Bin Files (For Users of Versions Prior to Version 3)

In Electronics Workbench version 1.x or 2, a circuit's parts bin was saved as a separate file with either a .LA or .LD extension. (Now the parts bin is saved with the circuit file.) Electronics Workbench version 3 and 4 will look for the parts bin file in the folder that contains the executable file (probably the Electronics Workbench folder).

When you load a circuit created in version 3, the old parts bin gets placed in the Custom bin.

Tip If you can't find a parts bin file, use Find File in the Apple menu to locate it.

Analysis of Circuits Created with an Earlier Version of Electronics Workbench (For Users of Versions Prior to Version 3)

Circuit analysis in Electronics Workbench version 4 is not the same as in earlier versions.

If you open a circuit created with an earlier version of Electronics Workbench, the analysis options are automatically switched to the most appropriate settings. For example, if your circuit used AC SS analysis (the default), the analysis option "Assume linear operation" is turned on, unless the circuit contains nonlinear components or uses a triangular or square waveform.

Appendix B
Sharing Circuits with PCs

Cross-Platform Transfer

Electronics Workbench runs on a Macintosh or on a PC with Windows or DOS. Circuits you create using Electronics Workbench on one platform can be used on another platform, without any file conversion or special formatting. All you need is a method of cross-platform transfer, so one computer can read the other computer's files.

Cross-platform transfer methods include sharing files over a network, sending files over E-mail, or using floppy disks to exchange files. If you want to transfer circuits using a floppy disk, you'll need a Macintosh with a floppy drive that can read DOS-formatted disks and software such as Apple File Exchange (which comes with System 7), Dayna Communications' DOS Mounter Plus or Insignia Solutions' AccessPC. If your Macintosh came with System 7, you'll find information on using Apple File Exchange in the *Macintosh User's Guide*. For information on other file-transfer methods, contact your dealer or refer to the documentation that comes with the product.

Transferring Macintosh Circuits to a PC

The procedure for transferring Macintosh circuits to either the Windows or DOS version of Electronics Workbench is the same. As long as a circuit file can be read by a PC, it can be opened with either version.

➤ To transfer a circuit to a PC:

1. Give the circuit a name that will be recognized by DOS. A DOS name can have up to eight characters and cannot include punctuation marks such as commas (,) or colons (:). Hyphens (-) or underscores (_) are ok. The circuit must have a .CA4 filename extension.

   For example, a circuit named DC DIVIDER could be renamed DCDIVIDE.CA4, while a circuit named Digital Gates might be renamed GATES.CA4.

2. Use one of the methods described at the beginning of this appendix to allow the circuit file to be read by a PC. (For example, if you are using a floppy disk and Apple File Exchange, initialize the disk in MS-DOS format, then copy the circuit onto the disk.)

3. Start either the Window or DOS version of Electronics Workbench. (If you are transferring an analog circuit, start the analog module. If you are transferring a digital circuit, start the digital module.)

4. Open the circuit using the Open command in the File menu.

Opening Circuits Created on a PC

➤ To open a circuit created on a PC:

1. Make sure your Macintosh can read the PC circuit file using one of the methods described at the beginning of this appendix.

2. Start Electronics Workbench if it is not already running.

3. Press the OPTION key and choose Open from the File menu.

4. Use the directory dialog box that appears to select and open the circuit. You can recognize PC circuit files by their filename extension — a period followed by a three-letter tag at the end of a circuit name. Version 4 circuits have a .CA4 extension; for example, DCDIVIDE.CA4.

5. If you want to give the circuit a different name, use the Save As command. Or rename the circuit on the desktop.

Index